Anne Mather

GREEN LIGHTNING

MILLS & BOON LIMITED
ETON HOUSE   18–24 PARADISE ROAD
RICHMOND   SURREY TW9 ISR

First published in Great Britain 1983
by Mills & Boon Limited

© Anne Mather 1983

Australian copyright 1983
Philippine copyright 1983
Reprinted 1983
This edition 1989

ISBN 0 263 76541 5

Set in Monophoto Plantin 10 on 11 pt
02–8910–54921

Printed and bound in Great Britain

CHAPTER ONE

SHE was waiting at the Bell corner when Helen turned into Castle Street. Helen knew it was her right off, even though she had never set eyes on her before. Heath had described her so accurately—blonde, willowy, elegant—everything Helen was not, and possessing the necessary qualities of a lady, which Helen was required to learn.

Compressing her lips, Helen brought the Land Rover to a squealing halt beside the kerb and regarded the newcomer mutinously. She had been tempted to come and meet her on the Honda, but her disregard for her uncle's wishes would only stretch so far, and already she had the underlying suspicion that by coming in the dusty Land Rover she was only reinforcing his opinion that she was irresponsible and childish.

Squashing these thoughts, Helen thrust open her door and got out, facing the young woman with grim determination. 'Miss Patterson?' she enquired, glancing at the two expensive suitcases standing beside her on the pavement. 'I'm Helen Mortimer.'

The young woman turned a decidedly haughty look in her direction. 'You are?' she exclaimed, her expression eloquent of her opinion that she had made a terrible mistake. 'You're Mr Heathcliffe's niece? My goodness, he wasn't exaggerating, was he?'

Helen's lips tightened over the retort she would have loved to have made. Instead she controlled her temper and said stiffly: 'If you'd like to get in . . .'

Miss Patterson's horrified blue eyes moved incredulously over the beaten-up vehicle. 'Into *that*? Where's Mr Heathcliffe?'

'He couldn't come.' Helen shifted her weight from one foot to the other. 'He sent me instead.'

'A baptism of fire, no doubt,' remarked Miss Patterson dryly. 'So where is your uncle?'

'Does it matter?'

Helen was rapidly losing any lingering sympathy she might have felt for the young woman. Miss Patterson's contemptuous appraisal was making her feel gauche and immature, and she was beginning to wish she had brought the Mercedes as Heath had directed. And worn something a little more flattering, she reflected unwillingly. Faded jeans and a sloppy tee-shirt might successfully demonstrate her desire for independence, but compared to the attractive cream and green pants suit Miss Patterson was wearing, they looked cheap and shabby. Even the silk scarf draped casually about Miss Patterson's neck must have cost more than her scuffed trainers, and the other girl's hair was fashionably short and smooth, curving lovingly in to the back of her neck.

'Are you saying your uncle sent you to meet me in— *this*?' Miss Patterson enquired now, causing Helen's nails to ball into her palms. 'How quaint! The original covered wagon, no doubt.'

Helen's colour deepened. 'Heath had to go to the office unexpectedly,' she declared aggressively. 'Shall we go?'

'Well . . .' Miss Patterson glanced about her doubtfully and Helen had the distinct impression that she half expected Heath to appear in spite of what had been said. Perhaps she thought *she* was playing at being chauffeur. It was obvious from her attitude, she thought miserably little of Helen's offer.

Walking round to get back into the driving seat, Helen schooled the errant impulse to drive away and leave her. If the Land Rover wasn't good enough, let her find her own way to Matlock, she thought broodingly, but a glance back at her charge made her make another attempt to be civil.

'Are you coming?' she asked, pulling open her door, and waiting with impatience for the other girl to move.

But Miss Patterson didn't move. Glancing down at her luggage with the air of someone unused to carrying anything heavier than a handbag, she lifted her shoulders indifferently, and Helen's resentment deepened at the obvious implication. Dammit, why couldn't the woman put her own suitcases into the Land Rover? she thought angrily. Time was passing, and she had no wish to meet Heath's car at the gates, or anticipate his undoubted fury when he discovered what she had done.

Miss Patterson shifted her handbag and jacket from one arm to the other and looked up and down the street, as if hoping divine providence might intervene. She still made no move to get into the Land Rover, and Helen's nerves tightened when she saw Father Kirkpatrick emerge from the Presbytery and start to walk in their direction. Heath was not a religious man, but he did occasionally have Father Kirkpatrick to dinner, and the last thing Helen needed now was the garrulous old priest to start questioning her for being there.

With a muffled curse, she came back round the vehicle and swinging open the passenger door, indicated that Miss Patterson should get inside. Then, with the resilience of youth, she tossed the two offending suitcases into the back of the Land Rover, before striding back to resume her seat.

Miss Patterson hesitated just long enough to put Helen's teeth on edge, and then, after examining the worn leather seat rather dubiously, she acquiesced. The door closed behind her only seconds before the shortsighted priest would have reached them, and the Land Rover's tyres sent up a cloud of dust as Helen made her getaway.

Not until she had put several hundred yards between them and embarrassing discovery did she relax, and Miss Patterson clung to her seat in dismay as the vehicle bounced recklessly along the High Street before swinging dangerously round the corner into Church Lane. The outskirts of the village were left behind within a few minutes, and Helen lifted her foot slightly as they crested Starforth Bank.

'Have you been driving long?' Miss Patterson enquired scathingly, when at last it seemed safe to distract Helen from her driving, and the younger girl nodded.

'Nine months,' she declared carelessly, refusing to rise to the bait. Matlock Edge, Heath's sprawling country estate, was only five miles from Starforth, and she refused to be disconcerted now when all around them the countryside she loved was unwinding in undulating curves.

'Nine months?' Miss Patterson sounded surprised. 'But I thought your uncle told me you'd only recently had your seventeenth birthday.'

'Six months ago, I did,' replied Helen defensively. 'But I've been driving around the estate roads for ages. I passed my test a month after my seventeenth birthday.'

'Really?' Miss Patterson did not sound impressed. 'I presume you learned to drive in tractors and the like.'

'No, in Heath's Mercedes, actually,' retorted Helen shortly. 'He taught me himself, when he had the time.'

'Heath?' Miss Patterson shook her head. 'You mean—Mr Heathcliffe, don't you? Your Uncle—Rupert?'

Helen sighed impatiently. 'Yes,' she agreed shrugging. 'But no one calls him Mr *Heathcliffe*. Well, practically nobody anyway. He doesn't care for it.'

'I wonder why?' Miss Patterson folded her jacket precisely. 'I think it's rather an attractive name. And so reminiscent of the area. I mean,' she went on carefully, 'this is Brontë country, isn't it? And Heathcliff was such a—marvellous character!'

Helen's skin prickled. 'Heath's not at all like his namesake,' she declared contemptuously. And then, with reckless abandon, she added: 'Is that why you've come here, Miss Patterson? Because you found my uncle attractive?'

'Why, you——' The ice-cool features slipped for just a moment, and then, with an effort, the other girl uttered a light laugh. 'Dear me,' she exclaimed, her tone at once provoking and mocking, 'no wonder your uncle feels you need some discipline! If you embarrass all his guests the way you just tried to embarrass me, I imagine he finds your presence rather tiresome!'

'You're not a guest,' declared Helen tensely, but her hands were damp where she was clutching the wheel. She really had done it now, she thought unhappily. Heath would be furious with her when he found out about her insolence, and the spectre of the school in Switzerland where he had threatened to send her moved one step nearer.

'I think you're wrong,' Miss Patterson was saying now, smoothing a pleat in her skirt. 'Your uncle made it quite clear that I was to be treated as a member of the family, and that your—instruction—was, for the most part, to take the form of correction, rather than actual teaching.'

Helen did not answer; she was too choked up. This was typical of Heath, she thought mutinously. To hire a glorified governess for her, and then to treat the governess as if she, and not Helen, was his prime concern. She didn't know what was the matter with Heath lately. He didn't used to be like this. But in the last year he had become really objectionable. He hardly ever took her out with him any more, and when he had visitors he didn't even ask her to join them for dinner. Once upon a time, he used to introduce her to all his friends, even the women who came and went in his life, and there had been a lot of them. Miss Patterson was right about one thing: Heath was an attractive man, and there had never been any shortage of females eager to show that they could be indispensable to him. But he'd never got married, even though she had overheard Cook telling Mrs Gittens that he should.

She used to hope that she might be responsible for that. During long nights at boarding school, she used to fantasize that Heath was only waiting for her to grow up to tell her he was madly in love with her. The other girls used to envy her in those days. When sports and speech days came around, all her friends wanted to be introduced to her handsome uncle, and she had lived for the holidays and the opportunities they gave her to be with him again. But it hadn't happened that way. Since she was sixteen and had begged to be allowed to leave school, he had increasingly found reasons to avoid her, and the culmination of her humiliation had been his denunciation of her as a responsible adult.

She supposed she was partly to blame for the poor opinion he had of her. It was true that his neglect had led her to look for ways to attract his attention—not always sensible ways either. When he bought her the Honda for her sixteenth birthday, he had not intended her to use it to ride along the wall bounding the vegetable garden, or to tumble ignominiously in among Mr Wesley's prize raspberries, successfully destroying the canes and tearing some of the bushes out at the roots. But it had been so boring riding the modest little machine up and down the roads of the estate, and she had been sure she could keep her balance.

The upshot of that had been that she was grounded

for a couple of months, and by the time she got the use of the motorcycle back again, much of the novelty had worn off. Six weeks later she had passed her test for the machine, and she had never been reckless enough to repeat such an episode.

Nevertheless, there had been other escapades: like climbing one of the apple trees in the orchard and pretending she couldn't get down. She had expected Heath would climb up to help her, but instead Mrs Gittens had called the fire brigade, and Helen had had the embarrassing experience of being carried down over a young fireman's shoulder like a sack of potatoes.

But the incident which had caused the most bother had happened only a few weeks ago. One hot evening in June, she had decided to take a midnight dip in the swimming pool, and Heath had caught her climbing out of the water, naked as the day she was born.

Glancing sideways now at the elegant figure of Miss Patterson, Helen reflected dourly that she had probably never gone skinny-dipping in her life. She couldn't imagine the immaculate Miss Patterson shedding the scales of civilisation, or see her dripping with water, her hair all wet and mussy. Touching her own rope of silky black hair, presently confined in a thick braid over one shoulder, Helen recalled how glad she had been of its length to hide her blushes, the harsh words that Heath had uttered making her want to die of shame and confusion.

The narrow lanes around Starforth gave on to the wooded beauty of Jacob's Hollow, and beyond, the valley of the River Pendle. To the south and west lay the industrial areas of Yorkshire and Lancashire, but Matlock Edge was set in the rolling beauty of the Pendle valley, whose only claim to the twentieth century was the tall stone chimneys of Deacon's Woollen Mill. Heathcliffes were in the textile trade, too. Heath's grandfather had founded the company, and Heathcliffe's Worsted had been produced in the West Riding since 1908. The fact that the West Riding was now West Yorkshire made little difference. Heathcliffe's Worsted still had a name for quality, and although Heath's father had diversified and Heath himself had interests in various other industries, the original mill continued production. It had been modernised, of course. Heath had used the profit from some of his other interests to maintain the standards of employment his grandfather had always insisted upon, and although other mills had had to close during the recent recession, Heathcliffe's had managed to keep their heads above water.

'Is it much farther?'

Miss Patterson's enquiry brought Helen out of her reverie, and glancing sideways at her passenger, she unwillingly shook her head. 'No,' she said, changing gear to negotiate the hazardous bends of Matlock Bank. Then, shrugging her shoulders carelessly, she added: 'That's the house, over there.' She pointed. 'It's only another mile to the entrance to the estate.'

The older girl surveyed the stone building outlined against the backdrop of fields and woodland with evident interest. And indeed, Matlock did look rather impressive, thought Helen uneasily. Who could fail to admire its irregular yet aristocratic lines, the walls even from this distance darkened by the flourishing creeper whose scented blossom pervaded the house with its perfume? It was the kind of house anyone might wish to own, and she had always felt proud to show people her home in the past. But Miss Patterson was different. Somehow, Helen had the feeling, this woman was going to bring unwelcome changes to her life, and she wished with all her heart that Heath had never espoused the idea of finding her a companion.

The house disappeared behind hedges as the road

levelled off at the foot of the bank, and Miss Patterson sank back in her seat, a faint smile lifting the corners of her mouth. 'So that's Matlock Edge,' she remarked half to herself. 'Your uncle must be a wealthy man.'

Helen did not respond. Gnawing at her lower lip, she was unhappily aware that her previous outburst about Miss Patterson's interest in her uncle had not been so wide of the mark, and whether or not she seriously considered herself a contender for the role of mistress of Matlock Edge, she certainly would not object to being entered in the lists. Helen's jaw jutted frustratedly. Heath couldn't be interested in Miss Patterson, could he? With so many other women to choose from, he wouldn't get involved with his niece's companion, surely! Helen's lips quivered. Why did it matter so much? she asked herself angrily. There had been women before; no doubt there would be women again. So why object so strongly to just another candidate for his bed?

The truth was that since she had left school, there had been no other women at Matlock Edge; at least, not for any length of time. The glamorous females who used to haunt the schoolroom when she was a little girl, and later on proffered gushing congratulations at her skill on the tennis court or her prowess at swimming, had given way in recent years to the wives and girl-friends of business colleagues, and she was no longer obliged to put on her party frock or recite her party piece in front of simpering felines who couldn't wait to get Heath into bed.

Helen wasn't exactly sure when she had realised that this was their objective. She had not been a particularly precocious child, at least, she didn't think so, but gradually, as her own body's processes started to mature, she began to understand why all those girls had hung about him. Heath was attractive—very attractive. He was tall and lean, not especially

muscular, but possessed of any easy grace of motion
that gave all his movements a peculiarly sexual appeal.
His hair was silvery fair—though his skin was not—
and smooth, requiring no artificial conditioner. His
features were slightly irregular—high cheekbones, a
nose that was not entirely straight, and a strong
uncompromising chin. But it was his eyes that gave his
face its sensual magnetism; set deep beneath hooded
lids and shaded by thick stubby lashes, they could
spear a person with living steel or melt an ice-cap with
emerald fire. Helen remembered those eyes first when
her parents died—her stepmother had been Heath's
only sister—and the three-year-old orphan had been
totally disarmed by their tender loving kindness. She
still recalled how he had gathered her into his arms
and carried her away from the memory of how her
parents had died, trapped in their car beneath the
wheels of an articulated lorry, and he had been
carrying her ever since, she brooded, in one way or
another . . .

The lodge gates stood wide, and old Jenkins, the
lodge-keeper, scratched his head disapprovingly as
Helen swept between them. No doubt he was
wondering where she had been with the Land Rover,
Helen thought impatiently, hoping his old eyes had
not glimpsed her passenger.

An expanse of sloping parkland separated the house
from the road, liberally swept with spreading oaks and
shady elms, ideal for the protection of privacy. Helen
knew that Heath's grandfather had bought the house
in the early part of the twentieth century, but although
its walls were Georgian its interior owed much of its
comfort to more recent innovations. Heath kept horses
in the park, and the grounds around the house were
private, but the rest of the estate was on lease to tenant
farmers, whose produce helped to make Matlock Edge
almost self-sufficient. They grew their own fruit and

vegetables, they slaughtered their own meat and poultry, and dairy produce was always fresh and delicious, owing nothing to artificial preservatives.

'Who else lives in the house?' Miss Patterson asked, as the Land Rover approached the white-painted gate that separated the garden of the house from the park. 'It's so big. It must have a dozen bedrooms! Surely you and your uncle don't live here alone?'

Helen's lips tightened. 'Why not?' she demanded, stepping on the brakes with more aggression than caution, and throwing the other girl forward in her seat. 'Heath and I don't need anyone else. Apart from the servants, of course.'

Miss Patterson took the time while Helen was climbing down and opening the gate to gather her composure, and when the younger girl got back into the Land Rover, she said tersely: 'You really must stop behaving like a schoolgirl. I imagine your uncle can't wait for someone to come and take you off his hands.'

Helen's jaw clenched. 'My *uncle*, as you call him, made a mistake when he employed you, Miss Patterson. And if I don't like you, you'll very soon be making the return journey to London.'

'I think not.' Miss Patterson was complacent. 'Mr Heathcliffe warned me that you might be difficult. He—er—he said you were a—spoilt brat, and that anything I could do to get you off his back was all right with him!'

'That's not true!'

The words burst from Helen's lips in angry denial, even as her brain warned her not to show her feelings to this woman. Whatever Heath had said, whatever she felt about it, she should not, she *must* not, let this Miss Patterson know she could get under her skin.

'I'm sorry, but it is true,' declared Miss Patterson smoothly, lifting a languid hand and gesturing behind them. 'Oughtn't you to close the gate? I doubt your uncle wants his horses wandering over his flower beds.'

Clenching her fists, Helen sprang out of the Land Rover, racing back to close the gate, blinking the smarting sting of tears from her eyes. Heath hadn't said that, she told herself fiercely, Heath *wouldn't* say that! But she was very much afraid he had!

It wasn't easy hiding her feelings from Miss Patterson. She had never tried to hide her feelings before, always acting instinctively, spontaneously, never dissimulating or concealing anything from Heath. She had thought he had been that way with her, too. She had never dreamt he had thoughts and feelings so dissimilar to her own. She had certainly never expected him to talk about her to a stranger, or to speak of her in such a contemptuous way. She felt hurt and humiliated, almost as humiliated as that night at the pool, and it wasn't easy to cope with this situation under the mocking eyes of Miss Patterson.

There was a sweep of gravel before the house, in the centre of which was a stone fountain. Helen drove the Land Rover grimly in the half circle it took to reach the front door, and then braked with rather more control before indicating that her passenger should alight.

Miss Patterson got out surveying her surroundings with evident pleasure. Her gaze absorbed the jutting façade that flanked the door and the windows on either side, then spread to the long wings, with their leaded, mullioned panes. Above the first floor, a tiled roof sloped to attic windows and tall chimneys, unused now, and acted as a backdrop to the arching façade.

'Beautiful!' Miss Patterson declared enthusiastically, and then turned, a smug smile lifting her lips, as the door behind her was suddenly opened.

Helen, about to steer the Land Rover round to the garages, froze in her seat, but it was only the homely form of the housekeeper that appeared. However, her scandalised gaze took in the newcomer in her elegant suit and behind her the dusty Land Rover, with Helen clutching the wheel.

'You didn't go to meet—oh, *Helen!*' Mrs Gittens exclaimed impatiently, and then came quickly down the shallow steps to meet the new employee. 'You must be Miss Patterson,' she added, holding out her hand. 'I hope you had a good journey. You must be tired after coming all that way.'

'It wasn't all that far, really,' Helen's adversary assured Mrs Gittens smoothly, allowing her hand to rest for just a second in that of the housekeeper. 'But I must admit I'm glad to be here. My spine feels as if it's been done some permanent damage!'

'The Land Rover's built for practical purposes, not for comfort,' Helen began, only to have Mrs Gittens give her a reproving look.

'I should go and put it away, if I were you,' she advised, eyeing her employer's niece with a knowing air. 'Mr Heathcliffe may be back directly, and I doubt he'll approve of your choice of vehicle to go and meet a visitor.'

Helen hunched her shoulders. 'Her cases are in the back,' she declared, making no attempt to remove them, and with a sound of impatience Mrs Gittens went back up the steps and summoned old Arnold Wesley to come and give a hand.

However, Helen could not let the old man haul the cases out single-handed. If it had been John Garnett, Mr Wesley's young apprentice, she would not have minded, but Arnold Wesley was only kept on because he had been at Matlock for more than fifty years. With a sign of frustration, she jumped out of the vehicle, dragged both cases out on to the gravel, and then jumped back in again and restarted the engine.

Miles Ormerod, who looked after the estate vehicles

and acted as chauffeur when the need arose, was in the garage yard, polishing the bronze Mercedes Helen was supposed to have taken to meet Miss Patterson. He grimaced when Helen stood on her brakes in the yard, and came round to open the Land Rover door for her as she switched off the engine.

'You look flushed,' he remarked as she got out, and Helen glared at him. As children, she and Miles had often played together in the fields and woods around Matlock, and that familiarity lingered still in a certain kind of affection.

'She's here,' Helen said now, thrusting her hands into the back hip pockets of her tight jeans. 'And she's just as repulsive as I expected.'

'Repulsive?' Miles looked surprised. 'I thought you said Heath described her as slim and blonde and——'

'Oh, he did!' Helen interrupted crossly. 'And she is. I just mean—well, she doesn't like me.'

'Don't you mean you don't like her?' asked Miles gently, propping himself against the bonnet of the Land Rover. At nineteen, he was two years her senior, but for all that, their eyes were almost on a level. Helen was a tall girl, though by no means as willowy as Miss Patterson, and in recent months she had seen a different look come into Miles' eyes when he was alone with her. She knew he found her attractive, and she thought he was attractive, too. But for so long Heath had occupied all her thoughts, and she seldom saw Miles as anything more than a good friend.

Now, however, she propped herself beside him, basking in the warmth of his understanding. Even Mrs Gittens had turned against her, she thought miserably, and if Miss Patterson told Heath about the Land Rover . . .

'What's wrong?'

Miles took the curling tail of her braid between his fingers and tugged sympathetically, and Helen turned to look at him. 'Why do you ask that?' she demanded, fighting back the impulse to confide in him, and his lips twisted wryly as he surveyed her troubled face.

'I know you pretty well by now,' he essayed quietly. 'I guess it was something this woman said. What's the matter? Did she tell you she and Heath are more than just friends? Oh, come on, Helen, it won't be the first time, will it? There've always been women around Matlock Edge.'

Helen's chin jutted. 'She said—she said Heath had said I was a spoilt brat,' she muttered in a low voice, then stared at Miles resentfully when he was unable to suppress his mirth. 'I didn't think it was funny!' she declared, straightening away from the Land Rover, and would have left him then, had he not turned and prevented her.

'But don't you see?' exclaimed Miles, imprisoning her with one hand on either side of her. 'You *are* a spoilt brat! That's why you're so choked up about it.'

'I am not!'

Helen was indignant, but looking into Miles' grinning face, she felt a corresponding response rising up inside her. 'You're a pig!' she muttered, pushing her fist into his midriff, and then sobered abruptly when he bent his head towards her.

His lips were soft and moist, pressing on hers with sudden urgency, but although Helen was glad of his friendship, this was a development she had not anticipated. It was true, they had fooled around a lot this year, and once or twice she had let him kiss her, but not like this. Now, Miles' lips were parting wetly, and his hand was groping clumsily for the full breasts outlined beneath the clinging material of her tee-shirt. He was pressing her against the side of the Land Rover, the metal was digging into her hips, and she realised with a sense of revulsion that he was becoming aroused.

'For God's sake, what the hell do you think you're doing?'

The harsh invective tore them apart as successfully as brute force might have done. Even so, Helen realised afterwards, Heath had only just been able to control the urge to strike the pair of them. Distracted, as she had been, by the unexpected fervour of Miles' embrace, she had failed to hear her uncle's car approaching, but turning now, she saw the dark green Porsche parked only feet away. Its door was still open where Heath had thrust it when he had emerged like a raging bull, and her eyes clung to the sleek lines of the vehicle to avoid looking into Heath's dark and furious face.

'I asked what the hell you thought you were doing,' he snarled now, taking a step towards Miles, who stood mutely to one side. 'Damn you, Ormerod, do I have to thrash an answer out of you? How long have you been familiar with my niece? How long has this been going on?'

'Nothing's going on, Heath,' mumbled Helen unwillingly, lifting her dark eyes to his face. She had never seen Heath so furious, and while she suspected it was mostly to do with her going to fetch Miss Patterson in the Land Rover, she didn't like the ugly look he was directing at Miles. 'Honestly. Miles was just—kissing me, that's all. Nothing to get so steamed up about.'

It wasn't exactly the truth, but right then she only wanted to relieve Miles of the responsibility for what had happened. After all, she had invited it. She had come here, begging for his sympathy. If she had got rather more than she bargained for, she couldn't entirely blame him for that.

As it happened, she might have saved her breath, however. Heath ignored her, stepping close to Miles, and forcing the younger man to tip his head to look at him. 'Just remember this,' he said savagely, 'if you so much as lay a finger on my niece again, I'll break your bloody neck! Do you hear me?'

'I hear you.' Miles pushed his lips forward in a desperate effort of defiance, but Heath was already turning away.

'Come with me,' he ordered Helen grimly, starting back towards the house, and with a little gesture of condolence to Miles, she had no choice but to obey.

CHAPTER TWO

PREPARING for dinner that evening, Helen found herself going over those stormy minutes with Heath again and again, trying to discover how it was everything had gone so wrong. If only he had not come upon her and Miles like that; if only she had not stumbled into explanations he had not asked for; if only she had acted a little more maturely, she might not be feeling so miserable now.

Sighing, she sank down on to the padded stool in front of her dressing table and surveyed her reflection with brooding disgust. Tears always left her looking all blotched and puffy around her eyes, and she had cried for an hour after Heath had let her go. Even her nose looked as if she was going down with a cold, and she doubted if even a heavy make-up could disguise what she had been doing.

Resting her elbows on the polished wood, she sniffed dejectedly. Why was it that she always came out of their arguments feeling like a victim, while Heath could dismiss her one minute and talk casually to Mrs Gittens the next? It wasn't fair! She wasn't a child any longer. But Heath persisted in treating her like one, and she always seemed to end up proving he was right.

It wasn't as if she had got angry with him for treating Miles like he had. On the contrary, if she was honest she would admit that she had been more than a little relieved when Heath had appeared, even if his entrance had precipitated another fight. Miles' behaviour had warned her of the dangers inherent in their relationship, particularly as she was not interested in him that way, and she thought she ought to be grateful to Heath for that.

Nevertheless, her uncle had not been prepared to forgive and forget. The minute they were out of earshot, he had turned his contemptuous gaze upon her, and his belittling appraisal had done nothing to restore Helen's self-confidence.

'How long?' he demanded, his green eyes raking her face with grim intent. 'How long has that oaf been allowed to touch you?'

'He didn't—he hasn't—I mean, it wasn't what you thought, Heath,' Helen started unhappily. 'It was just—well, when I brought the Land Rover back, he—he sympathised with me.' She tucked her chin against her chest. 'I—I suppose I asked for it.'

Heath halted abruptly by the gate leading into the orchard. 'What do you mean? Had you had an accident in the Land Rover? I've warned you about driving too fast before——'

'I wasn't driving too fast,' protested Helen helplessly. 'And I didn't have a crash.'

'Why would he need to sympathise with you, then?' Heath grated, his lean face taut with impatience. 'What's happened, Helen? What have you done? You might as well tell me, before Mrs Gittens does.'

Helen lifted her face unwillingly. Comprehension was dawning, and she didn't like what she was thinking. 'You mean—you mean—you haven't seen Mrs Gittens?'

'No. I drove straight to the garage. Why?'

'Oh, God!' Helen's shoulders sagged. 'But—I thought you knew. I thought that was why you were so mad——'

'I knew? I knew what?' snapped Heath irritably, grasping her by the shoulders. 'For heaven's sake, Helen, get to the point. What is it I'm supposed to know?'

Helen shook her head. 'Don't you remember?'

'Remember what?'

'Where—where you asked me to go this afternoon?'

'Where I asked you to go?' declared Heath blankly. 'No, damn you, I don't—*yes*! Hell, yes, of course I do!' He stared down into her troubled face with growing comprehension. 'The Land Rover!' he snarled. 'You went to meet Angela Patterson in the Land Rover!' His fingers dug painfully into the soft flesh of her upper arms. 'Lord, I'd forgotten all about her!'

That was reassuring, at least, thought Helen tremulously, but her reassurance was shortlived. Her words had driven every trace of warmth out of Heath's face, and the hard green eyes were like lasers boring into her.

'You little bitch!' he swore violently. 'You self-willed little hellion! You deserve a damn good hiding, and one of these days I'm going to give it to you!'

His ill-chosen words brought her back from the brink of self-pity, and dragging together what little confidence she had left, she faced him bravely. 'It'll take a better man than you, Rupert Heathcliffe!' she declared courageously, and tearing herself out of his grasp, she ran the rest of the distance to the kitchen door. There was a back staircase that led from the kitchen to the upper floors of the house, and ignoring Cook's startled face, Helen took it. She doubted Heath would follow her, and she was right; but she didn't stop until the door of her room was closed securely behind her.

Now she got up from the stool and surveyed her domain with troubled eyes. It was more than three hours since she had had that confrontation with Heath, and she was dreading the prospect of joining him and Angela Patterson for dinner. Mrs Gittens had brought her this news, tapping tentatively at Helen's door and clucking her tongue reprovingly when she saw Helen's tearful face.

'You should have known better,' she declared, tidying

up the clothes Helen had left strewn across the soft pink carpet, and shaking her head at the silk wrapper which was all the girl was wearing. 'You'd better get some clothes on. Your uncle's sent me to tell you he expects you to join him for dinner this evening. He wants you to meet the young lady who arrived this afternoon.'

'I have met her,' muttered Helen sulkily, sitting crosslegged on her bed, but Mrs Gittens only gave her an old-fashioned look.

'From what I hear, you refused to speak courteously to the young woman,' she responded drily. 'And if you don't want Heath coming up here and dragging you down by the hair, I'd suggest you made a little effort to be civil.'

Helen sighed now, running the tips of her fingers across the quilted damask covering the wide bed. She supposed she would have to change into something suitable for the evening, but how she wished she dared ignore the summons. The idea of eating dinner in Angela Patterson's company was not appealing, and whatever Heath said, she would never forgive him for speaking to her the way he had.

Her room at Matlock Edge overlooked the side and back of the house. Away to her right, the wooded slopes of Jacob's Hollow cast long shadows as the evening sank into dusk, and bats had started their wild erratic swooping between the trees. Below her, at the back of the house, were the tennis lawns and swimming pool, the trellises that hid the changing cabins from view bright with creamy yellow roses.

The room itself was spacious, and the furnishings matched their surroundings—long fitted wardrobes, a square dressing table, with leaved mirrors, and a huge bed, big enough to accommodate half a dozen people.

Helen remembered how lost and frightened she had felt when Heath first deposited her in that bed. But he

had always been able to soothe her baby fears away.
She knew he had stayed with her many nights, nights
when she had awakened screaming from a terrifying
nightmare to find he was there to comfort and reassure
her. Later, when he had returned to his own room, she
had missed his calming influence, but she had always
known he was just along the corridor, and she could
always go to him if she was frightened.

His mother had objected, of course. Mrs Heathcliffe
had still been living at Matlock Edge in those days.
Her husband, Heath's father, had died suddenly when
Heath was only nineteen, and he had left university to
come and handle his father's affairs. Heath had been
twenty-one when Helen came to live with him and his
mother, and Mrs Heathcliffe had lost no opportunity
to deride his reckless decision.

'It's not as if the child's a blood relative!' she had
argued. 'People will talk, Rupert!'

His mother was one of the few people who still
called him Rupert, but her pleas had been to no avail.
Heath had been adamant. Helen's father had had no
living relatives, and Heath and his mother were the
only people able to claim a relationship with the child,
the only people between Helen and a life in Council
care.

Scrubbing fiercely at the unwanted dampness of her
cheeks, Helen slid back the doors of the fitted
wardrobes and surveyed the rack of clothes. Thank
goodness Mrs Heathcliffe didn't live with them any
more, she thought fervently. Heath's mother had
never approved of her son's decision, and had lost no
opportunity to try and make the girl regret that she
had been brought to Matlock Edge.

As the years went by, Helen learned to ignore the
petty slights, the studied insults, the painful jabs in
the ribs Mrs Heathcliffe used to administer if she was
sure her son was out of the room, and eventually,

when she was ten, Heath's mother had taken herself
off to live in Manchester. She had an apartment there,
and Heath visited her dutifully every month, but
Helen's continued existence had caused a rift between
them that was difficult to breach. Even so, Mrs
Heathcliffe was not unhappy in Manchester. She
played golf and bridge, and she took regular trips
abroad for her health, or so she said, but privately
Helen thought it suited her to let Heath feel she had
been hurt by his loyalty to the child, as she had always
dubbed her. He was so much more generous that
way.

The clothes confronting her did not inspire any
enthusiasm. Helen much preferred jeans, or slacks of
any kind, to the more feminine items in her wardrobe,
and in consequence, the clothes she possessed were
mostly out of date. She so seldom ate dinner with
Heath these days, she had taken to having her evening
meal brought up to her room, preferring to curl up in
front of the portable television to facing a lonely hour
in the morning room. On those occasions when she
did join Heath for dinner, she had generally worn a
blouse and skirt, but somehow she knew Angela
Patterson would not appear at dinner dressed so
prosaically.

On impulse, she pulled out one of the party dresses
she had worn less than two years ago. A flouncy thing,
made of some synthetic fibre, it had not suited her
even then, but after wearing school uniform all day, it
had seemed a pleasant relief. Now, however, she saw it
for what it was: a puerile attempt to make a gauche
adolescent into a soignée adult, and she grimaced at
her own taste in choosing it.

Sighing, she allowed her hand to brush lightly along
the row of garments. What else did she have? she
asked herself unhappily. If she had asked Heath for
new clothes, no doubt he would have bought them for

her, but she had been too busy showing off on her
motorcycle to realise that proving herself as a woman
was more important than aping Heath's abilities. It
was too late now. She had to wear something from this
collection, and if she didn't hurry up, Heath would
have something else to get angry about.

A quick shower freshened her body, and rummaging
in her drawer for clean panties, she returned to her
appraisal of the wardrobe. If she wore any of these
she would be a laughing-stock, she thought, pulling
off a flimsy flowered nylon, which had crushed her
breasts in such a way it was practically indecent. She
would have to wear a blouse and skirt, as before, and
hope that Angela Patterson did not appear in
something too dissimilar.

She was fumbling with the buttons of her blouse
when the door opened behind her, and expecting Mrs
Gittens, she turned with an appealing grimace. 'I
know, I know,' she was beginning, 'but I can't seem to
get these buttons fastened——' and then she broke off
abruptly as Heath let himself into the room.

He had changed for dinner, into a lightweight dark
brown suit that complemented the darkness of his skin
and the silvery lightness of his hair. It clung to his
lean frame with loving elegance, accentuating the
supple lines of his body and the powerful length of his
legs.

'Oh!'

Helen turned sharply when she saw who it was,
bending her head deliberately to concentrate on her
task. But not before she had noticed, with some relief,
that he was no longer glaring angrily at her.

'Here, let me,' he offered briefly, coming behind
her, so that for a moment their reflections mingled in
the lamplit illumination of the dressing table mirrors.

'No. I mean—you can't,' muttered Helen, more
thumbs than fingers now with him watching her, and

growing impatient, he laid his hands on her shoulders and turned her round to face him.

'Why can't I?' he demanded, brushing her clumsy hands aside and deftly inserting buttons into holes. But she noticed that when his fingers accidentally touched her breast he withdrew his hand immediately, turning his eyes away from the sudden tautness of its crest.

He left her then, walking across the room half impatiently, as if unwilling to say what must be said. But finally he turned and faced her, and a little of the anger he had exhibited earlier was back there in the agate hardness of his eyes.

'Look,' he said at last, 'I guess we were both a little reckless this afternoon. I spoke—hastily, I admit it. I'm not saying it wasn't warranted. It was. But—well,' he thrust one hand to the back of his neck, 'I didn't mean to hurt you the way I did.'

Helen's lips trembled, and she turned her back on him again to unfasten the strip of leather holding the end of her braid in place. 'Who says you hurt me?' she asked, her voice annoyingly unsteady, and Heath uttered a muffled oath before striding back to where she was standing.

'Mrs Gittens told me you'd been crying,' he essayed quietly.

'Oh—Mrs Gittens!' Helen tugged fiercely at the hair she was releasing from the braid.

'Yes, Mrs Gittens,' agreed Heath, once more putting her hands aside and taking over. He allowed the thick silky hair to slide sensuously through his fingers. 'I suppose I was speaking out of turn. You'll be eighteen next year. Old enough to get married, if you want to. Certainly too old for me to object if you choose to allow young Ormerod to kiss you.'

'Oh, don't be silly!' Helen tore her hair out of his grasp and reached for her brush. For a moment, she had thought he was regretting his anger over her treatment of Miss Patterson. Instead, he was actually condoning the way Miles had treated her! 'I'm not interested in "young Ormerod", as you call him!' she snapped. 'Don't patronise me, Heath. You're not my father!'

'Maybe not. But I am old enough to be so,' he retorted, his own tone responding to the sharpness of hers. 'Anyway, as it seems obvious you don't desire my forgiveness, I'll go, and allow you to complete your toilette.'

The trace of mockery in his words was not lost on Helen, and she longed to say something to wipe that look of smugness from his face. But it would not do to antagonise him yet again, particularly with the prospect of the evening looming ahead of her like a visit to the dentist.

So instead, she said: 'Thank you,' and allowed him to walk to the door before adding in an undertone: 'I'm glad you're not still cross with me, Heath.'

'I don't remember saying I wasn't,' he retorted, his mouth twisting in acknowledgement of her counter-action. 'I just want you to know I'm not indifferent to the fact that you're growing up.'

Helen turned, her hair curling irrepressibly about her shoulders, her face suddenly alight with sudden hope. 'Do you think so?' she exclaimed. 'Do you really think so?'

'Yes,' he agreed flatly. 'You make me feel quite old,' and before she could respond, he had let himself out of the room.

Dinner was just as awful as Helen had anticipated.

They ate in the family dining room, which was one of the smaller rooms at Matlock Edge, with a circular dining table that dated from the eighteenth century. In daylight, the dining room looked out over the patio at the back of the house, but tonight the lamps were lit, and only the urns of flowers that flanked the french windows were illuminated from inside.

The dining room was panelled in oak, with delicately-carved clusters of rosebuds decorating the wood. The ceiling was high and moulded, and although there was a crystal and bronze chandelier suspended over the dining table, they mostly ate by lamp or candlelight, on those occasions when Heath had company.

As Helen had expected, Angela Patterson was present at the dinner table, sleek and self-satisfied in an ice-blue chiffon creation that left a good deal of her shoulders bare. She was not tanned, as Helen was tanned, from days spent almost exclusively outdoors. Her skin was white, whiter than any skin Helen had ever seen before, and smooth as alabaster, and just as soft.

In her white blouse and dark blue pleated skirt, Helen felt as if she was wearing school uniform again, and she guessed Miss Patterson was enjoying the evident contrast between them. It made her wish she had worn the floral nylon after all. At least then Heath would have been forced to notice her. With her burgeoning young body bursting from every seam, he could hardly have failed to do so.

It soon became obvious that Angela Patterson had made good use of the time Helen had spent sulking in her room. She and Heath were already on the best of terms, and Helen wouldn't have been at all surprised if Miss Patterson had called him Rupert. But she didn't. She addressed him as Mr Heathcliffe, though she spoke his name with a certain air of intimacy, and the conversation between them was relaxed and easy, as if they had known one another for years, instead of just hours.

'How fortunate for me that I went to Matt Hodge's

party,' Heath remarked, while Helen was making an effort to swallow the mouthful of lamb she had been chewing for the past three minutes. 'He and I are not exactly friends, more business associates, and it was only because I wanted to speak to him about a certain export order that I went along.'

'It was fortunate for me, too,' responded Angela Patterson eagerly. 'I mean, I didn't know what I was going to do. The rent on my apartment was due, and as you know, my qualifications don't exactly equip me for any ordinary job.'

'What are your qualifications, Miss Patterson?' Helen interspersed politely, ignoring Heath's sudden intake of breath, and the older girl uttered a tolerant laugh.

'Oh, I'm afraid, like you, I was brought up expecting not to have to work. Mr father was a successful author, of technical books, you understand——' this for Heath's benefit, Helen was sure—'but when he died, the death duties were crippling. I'm afraid I was left almost destitute, my only accomplishments to dress well and look pretty!'

She turned helpless eyes on Heath as she said this, and Helen wanted to curl up with embarrassment. Dear heaven, she thought, did Angela really think she could get away with *that*? Surely no one could expect to make such a statement without being laughed out of sight. But apparently Heath had accepted it, for, as Helen was gazing at her incredulously, he went on:

'The ideal accomplishments so far as I'm concerned. I suppose I am to blame for allowing Helen to persuade me that she was happy here at Matlock, doing nothing but race that noisy machine of hers. It's time she began to look like my niece, not to mention act like it. I'm beginning to believe my mother was not so far wrong when she said I was letting her grow up like a gipsy.'

Helen gasped, but before she could speak, Angela added: 'Yes. Well, I only hope she's prepared to listen to me. One can only teach when there is a willingness to learn.'

'Oh, I'm sure she will,' remarked Heath infuriatingly, raising his wine glass to his lips, and Helen's jaw clenched at this deliberate attempt to provoke her. They were speaking as if she wasn't there, and she had what she recognised as a childish desire to storm out of the room. But she didn't. She remained where she was, lifting her wine glass to Heath in a mocking kind of salute, so that his mockery faded to a brooding preoccupation.

'You have such a beautiful home,' Angela interjected, and Helen guessed she had noticed Heath's sudden lapse of interest in herself. 'Has it been in your family for a number of years? I noticed the exquisite carving on the stairs. Is it Grinling Gibbons?'

'A contemporary of his, I believe.' Heath recovered his manners, and forced a faint smile. 'Actually, the house was bought by my grandfather in the early part of this century. Before that, it was owned by the Countess of Starforth.'

'How interesting!' Angela finished eating and leant towards him confidingly. 'Daddy and I used to own a house in Cornwall—Trenholme. He bought it when my mother died. He found he could work there more easily than in London. He had so many friends, you know, and one or other of them was always calling in to see him when he was in town. That was why we moved away, really. He needed solitude for his writing.'

'I'm surprised one of your father's friends couldn't offer you a job,' put in Helen staunchly, determined not to be ignored completely. 'I mean, that's what friends are for, isn't it? To help you when you're desperate.'

Angela's lips thinned. 'I wasn't—desperate exactly, Helen. As—as a matter of fact, there were several positions offered to me. But it was finding the *right* job that mattered.' She exchanged a knowing smile with Heath. 'You understand, don't you, Mr Heathcliffe? A girl of my upbringing—well, it was important for me to find an occupation I could feel comfortable in.'

Heath nodded. 'I appreciate that.'

'What you're saying is, you wouldn't have scrubbed floors, or manned the check-out at a supermarket,' Helen persisted annoyingly, and she saw Angela's nails digging into her palms as she endeavoured to answer her civilly.

'There was no question of that,' she declared, casting another tolerant look in Heath's direction, but having got her enemy retreating, Helen was in no mood to let her go.

'I don't see what else you could have done,' she observed reasonably, folding her hands demurely in her lip. 'I mean, you did say you had no qualifications——'

'That will do, Helen.' Heath's abrupt remonstration brought her brief bid for superiority to an end. 'I'm sure you know perfectly well what Miss Patterson is talking about——'

'Oh—Angela, *please*!'

'Very well, then, Angela. I'm sure you understand what Angela is trying to say, Helen. And while we're on the subject, let me say I expect you to treat our guest with rather more courtesy than you've shown this far. I've apologised for your arriving to meet her in the Land Rover, and Angela's prepared to forgive and forget. So am I, providing we don't have any further demonstrations of that kind—do I make myself clear?'

'Perfectly,' exclaimed Helen tautly, her face burning

with hot colour. 'And now, as you evidently don't need my presence to discuss my shortcomings, perhaps you'll allow me to go to bed. I'm feeling rather tired.'

Heath's mouth tightened. 'Helen——' he said warningly, but she had thrust back her chair and was facing him with grim defiance. 'Oh, all right,' he muttered, lifting his expensively-groomed shoulders. 'Go to bed. I'll talk to you again in the morning.'

It was an effort to bid goodnight to Angela Patterson, but Helen managed it, leaving the room with her head held high, as much to hold back the tears as to demonstrate her independence. It had been a disaster. The day had been a disaster. And she was very much afraid that tomorrow and all the days after were not going to be that much better.

CHAPTER THREE

NIKO crunched the lump of sugar Helen had brought for him and nuzzled at her pocket for more. 'I'm sorry, boy,' she murmured, rubbing her face against his soft muzzle. 'I don't have any more.' She drew back to smile at him. 'You should be grateful! Sugar is awfully bad for your teeth.'

Niko whinnied softly in her ear, catching the collar of her shirt between his teeth and tugging affectionately. He was Heath's horse really, but he had been the recipient of all Helen's troubles ever since he came to Matlock Edge, and although the stable hands were wary of him, he had always been the soul of patience with her.

It was a shame no one did much riding at Matlock any more, she reflected. When she was little, Heath had bought her a pony and taught her to ride, and together they had combed the hills and valleys of the West Riding. But since she had grown older, Heath always said he was too busy to go riding with her, and if ever she did get the chance to ride with him, it was always in company with guests he had invited to the house. In earlier days, she had ridden alone from time to time, sometimes persuading the groom, Angus McLintock, to saddle Niko for her. But she knew he worried every time she rode out on her own, and he was relieved when Heath found out and put a stop to it.

Besides, latterly, she had had the Honda to get about the estate, and once she was seventeen and had learned to drive a car, she had neglected the horses. But she always came to Niko when she needed to confide her problems, and she sighed a little dejectedly at the realisation that this was the most serious problem yet.

The sound of men's voices aroused her from her absorption, and she straightened a little resentfully when she recognised Heath's deeper tones. It was scarcely seven a.m. Couldn't he at least have allowed her this time alone? Was she to have no privacy now that Angela Patterson had come to live in the house?

Although the voices were audible, she could not hear what was being said, though she guessed Angus McLintock would waste no time in telling his employer she was here. It was a mercy Niko had been installed in the stables overnight. Perhaps she could slip out the back way without Heath even seeing her. But the sudden darkening of the doorway kept her rooted to the spot, though she refused to turn and wish him good morning as if last night had never happened.

'Helen!' His attractively low-pitched use of her name almost made her relent, but she continued to stroke Niko's head, ignoring his sound of impatience, 'Helen, I want to talk to you. Have the decency to turn round and face me!'

Helen turned round abruptly, spreading her arms along the wooden rails at either side of her, facing him mutinously. 'Well?' she said insolently. 'What do you want? Have you invited Miss Patterson to go riding with you, and you want me to go along as chaperone? I'm sorry, I don't feel like riding today.'

Heath regarded her through narrowed lids. In a dark green corded jerkin and matching corded pants, he looked unconscionably attractive, and a curious pain stirred in the pit of her stomach as she met his concentrated gaze.

'Now, that's a pity,' he remarked. 'Because I was

going to invite you to go riding. But naturally, if you don't feel like it . . .'

Helen's lips compressed indignantly. 'I don't believe you.'

'It's what you said, not me.'

'No, you know what I mean.' She moved her head to avoid Niko's affectionate nuzzling. 'I don't believe you intended to take me riding. You're not even dressed for it.'

Heath shrugged. 'I can ride in these clothes as well as any others.' His mouth curved. 'Do I take it you would like to go riding after all?'

She shrugged, looking down at the legs of her cotton dungarees. 'Is Miss Patterson invited?'

'No.'

'No?' She looked up.

'No,' he agreed, glancing behind him into the yard. 'Now, do you want to go or don't you? I don't have that much time.'

Helen withdrew her arms from their defiant stance and sniffed. 'I suppose so.'

'Okay.' Heath stepped to one side. 'You'll find McLintock's already saddled Marnie. You go and find him while I attend to Niko.'

She stopped beside him indignantly. 'You were so sure I'd come, weren't you?'

Heath stepped past her. 'Stop wasting time,' he advised shortly. 'I've got to be in Bradford by ten o'clock.'

Helen wanted to refuse. She wanted to tell him to go ride himself, but she didn't. It was an opportunity of being alone with him she couldn't bear to miss, and she was waiting on Marnie's back when he led the black hunter out of its stall.

A gate beyond the stable yard gave access to the fields and parkland surrounding Matlock Edge. Helen had known Heath take that gate in full stride, but this morning he leant down to open it, allowing both horses through before re-securing the catch.

It was a glorious morning, the sun already giving some hint of the warmth of the day to come. Helen thought there was nowhere like England on an early summer morning, and although Heath had taken her to France and Italy, she still preferred the English countryside to those hotter foreign beaches.

Giving Marnie his head, she allowed the animal to take her at a gallop across the sloping meadow, hearing the low thunder of Niko's hooves behind her. For the moment, at least, Heath was prepared to give himself up to the enjoyment of the ride, and contentment spread, like wildfire, throughout her whole body. But eventually he caught up with her, exhibiting with ease the hunter's superior strength, and leaning across, reined Marnie in beside him.

'Right,' he said, 'let's talk, shall we? Pleasant as this is, I do have work to do.'

Helen hesitated a moment and then pointed to the thin ribbon of water flowing over rocks some few yards ahead of them. 'Let's dismount and sit by the stream,' she suggested, already digging her heels into Marnie's sides to urge him forward, and after a brief pause Heath followed her.

'All right,' he said, 'if this suits you. Personally, I'd prefer to stay in the saddle. The grass is wet.'

'It's only dew,' exclaimed Helen, sliding down from Marnie's back. 'Hmm, it smells delicious. Don't you think so?'

Heath shrugged, swinging his leg across the pommel and jumping down beside her. 'I can think of sweeter things,' he remarked drily, avoiding some wild creature's droppings, and walking to the edge of the water. 'You know I used to fish here, when I was little. I never could understand why I never caught anything.'

'Perhaps you used the wrong bait,' said Helen, coming to stand beside him. 'I used to paddle here, when Mrs Gittens would let me.' She grinned up at him. 'She was once livid because I stripped all my clothes off.'

Heath looked down at her drily. 'You have a habit of doing that, don't you?' he observed, and her cheeks turned pink. 'It's one of the things I'm hoping Angela will cure you of. That, and a few other practices we won't go into now.'

Helen pursed her lips. 'Is that why you brought me here? To talk about Angela Patterson?'

'Among other things,' he conceded, ignoring her sudden tension. 'You must have guessed that was what I wanted. I think you need to understand the situation.'

'Oh, I understand the situation all right,' muttered Helen tautly. 'You made it perfectly clear last night. I'm to learn to do as I'm told and keep my mouth shut. Isn't that a fair description of the situation?'

'No, it's not.' Heath spoke with some heat. 'Helen, you're not trying to be reasonable. I invited Angela Patterson to Matlock Edge to teach you the things a mother might have taught you—to help you to dress, how to act in company, how to behave like the lady I thought I'd brought you up to be. It wasn't intended to deteriorate into a slanging competition. I'd hoped you might like one another. And I still have hopes of that, even though you tried last night to make Angela look stupid!'

'I didn't have to try very hard, did I?' demanded Helen tensely, aware that the tears she had shed yesterday had by no means drained the reservoir. 'You can't believe all that stuff she told you about jobs and everything! I don't believe she's even looked for one. She was just waiting for someone like you.'

'It really doesn't matter whether I believe it or not,'

said Heath surprisingly, pushing his hands into the pockets of his pants.

'What do you mean?'

'Angela Patterson's history is of no particular interest to me.'

Helen frowned. 'But if she was lying——'

'Helen!' He turned to her then, shaking his head half impatiently when he saw the tears glistening in her eyes. 'I know all about Angela. You don't imagine I'd let a stranger come to live in my house without checking her out first?'

'You mean——'

'I mean I want you to listen to her. I want you to learn from her. And the first thing I want you to do is go with her to Manchester and let her choose you some new clothes. Feminine clothes,' he added, surveying the dungarees with evident distaste. 'I've neglected my duties too long. I should never have let you persuade me to let you leave school.'

Helen felt a glimmer of hope. 'You mean you're going to spend more time with me?' she asked, allowing her slim fingers to curve impulsively about his sleeve. 'Oh, Heath I'm sorry if I've made a fool of myself. I didn't realise what you were doing.' And then, before he could draw his hands out of his pockets to prevent her, or step back out of reach, she stretched up on her toes and kissed him, her eager lips seeking and finding his startled mouth.

Because he had been about to speak, his lips were parted, and she had to part her lips, too, to accommodate them. It was intended to be a kiss of gratitude, no more, a simple pressure to show him she intended to turn over a new leaf and behave as he wanted, but it didn't turn out that way. His lips were so firm and dry, utterly unlike Miles Ormerod's wet mouth, and the impulsive salutation was more pleasing than she had imagined. Instinctively, her own lips moved and deepened under his.

She heard Heath groan deep in his throat, and she thought for a moment he was in pain. But the sudden pressure that met her tentative caress seemed to negate such a suspicion, and the hands torn from his pockets reached for her, not to push her away.

Her head swam beneath that expert response. His mouth was hard now, and intimate, his hand at her nape holding her there, bruising the sensitive skin. It was not like the times Miles had kissed her, not like the way Heath had kissed her in the past. But she didn't want him to stop. She wanted him to go on and on, and her hands clung desperately to the lapels of his jerkin.

'*God!*'

She didn't know how long it was before Heath thrust her away from him. It had seemed like minutes, but she suspected it was only seconds. From the expression on his face, she doubted he could have prolonged the incident, and for the first time in her life she was too embarrassed to look at him.

'Who taught you to do that?' he asked her harshly, after a few moments, grasping her roughly by the chin and forcing her to look up at him. 'Ormerod, I suppose. God Almighty, and I thought you were only a child!'

Helen quivered. 'Miles didn't teach me,' she mumbled indignantly, but Heath was unconvinced.

'Who, then?' he demanded. 'Have there been other young men I don't know about? For God's sake, Helen, tell me, before I break your bloody neck!'

'Jealous?'

Helen spoke recklessly, hating him when he treated her like this, and Heath's expression darkened angrily. 'No,' he said grimly. 'No, I'm not jealous. How could I be jealous of a provocative teenager? But the next time you try something like that, I really will put you over my knee!'

Helen pulled her chin out of his grasp. 'I don't know what you're making all the fuss about,' she exclaimed chokingly. 'No harm's done.'

'Isn't there?' Heath grasped Niko's reins and swung himself up into the saddle. 'You're already making me regret my decision to bring Miss Patterson to Matlock Edge. I should have sent you to Switzerland as my mother suggested. At least there, you wouldn't have been my responsibility!'

Helen sniffed. 'I thought you liked it,' she muttered almost under her breath, but he heard her.

'I won't answer that,' he grated, turning his mount around. 'Come on, let's get back to the house. Perhaps Angela Patterson will succeed where I've failed.'

In the past, Helen had only ever visited Manchester on those rare occasions when Heath had taken her to visit his mother. It did not, therefore, have good associations for her, and going there in the company of Angela Patterson was no better. They had accomplished the journey in the bronze Mercedes, with Miles Ormerod at the wheel, and Helen was already chafing at the restrictions Heath had put upon her before they even parked the car. Since the affair by the stream that morning, she had seen nothing more of her uncle, but his warning about the school in Switzerland had not gone unheeded, and she was doing her utmost to behave as he would wish.

As soon as he had showered and changed, Heath had taken himself off to his business meeting in Bradford, without even so much as a cup of coffee, according to Mrs Gittens. 'Just got in his car and drove away,' she told Helen severely, as she served her her breakfast in the morning room. 'His face was black as thunder—what had you been saying to him? I'd stake my life it was something to do with you and that little outing you took earlier on.'

'I really don't know,' Helen had affirmed determinedly, her fingers crossed below the level of the
tablecloth. This was something she could not discuss
even with Mrs Gittens, who had taken care of her
since she was a toddler. No matter how mad Heath
made her, she would never confide her feelings about
him to anyone.

Angela Patterson appeared during the meal, slim
and delectable in a sleeveless shirtwaister and cream
strappy sandals. 'I only ever drink coffee in the
mornings,' she had assured Mrs Gittens, after
surveying Helen's plate of scrambled eggs with a
faintly horrified eye. 'Some of us need to count the
calories,' she had added, for the younger girl's benefit,
and Helen, whose appetite had suffered by the
morning's upheaval, abruptly lost all interest in the
food.

It had been awful having to remain at the table
while Angela drank her way through three cups of
black coffee and asked various questions about the
routine at Matlock Edge. Bearing Heath's warning in
mind, Helen had been politely civil, and Angela had
responded by giving a smug little smile now and then,
as if she knew perfectly well why Helen was on her
best behaviour.

When she had finally had enough, Mrs Gittens
suggested that Helen should show Miss Patterson
around the house, to acquaint her with the where-
abouts of the living rooms and so on. But Angela had
soon grown bored with looking into the library and the
music room, and the blue and gold elegance of the
drawing room, and had suggested a tour of the
gardens might give her a better understanding of
the layout of the house.

Shrugging, Helen had dutifully led her outside,
showing her the tennis and croquet lawns, allowing
her to admire the delicate tracery of the sunhouse,

which Heath's grandfather had had erected for his wife when she fell ill in 1924.

Evidently the kidney-shaped swimming pool met most with Angela's approval, and at her suggestion, the two girls changed into swimsuits and spent some time playing in the water.

'That hair will really have to be cut,' Angela declared, when they climbed out to sun themselves on the cushioned loungers set on the mosaic tiling of the patio. Watching Helen squeezing the water out of the silken rope, she shook her head disapprovingly. 'Long hair's out of fashion now, anyway,' she added. 'I think we'll have it cut, something like mine.'

Helen didn't make any response, although the idea of having all her hair cut off was not appealing. She had always had long hair. She liked long hair. But if that was what Heath wanted, what could she do about it?

Angela's appraisal of her body was disturbing, too. It made Helen uncomfortably aware that last year's bikini no longer provided an adequate covering, and the burgeoning fullness of her breasts had begun to overspill the skimpy bra. But last year she had not had this problem, and as soon as she could, she made herself scarce and went to change.

At lunch, Angela concentrated on finding out more about Heath's lifestyle. With the excuse of needing the information to equip Helen for the future, she successfully discovered that her uncle was a member of the board of several different companies, and that as well as Matlock Edge and the apartment in London, he also owned a villa in the South of France and a *palazzo* in Venice.

'How delightful,' she remarked, her tongue circling her lips as if in anticipation. 'You were a lucky girl to be adopted by him. Not all uncles are so generous.'

'Heath didn't adopt me,' exclaimed Helen shortly,

stung by the unknowing reminder of their relationship. 'My name is Mortimer—I told you. Heath's sister married my father.'

'Does it matter?' Angela was not particularly interested in their relationship. 'I doubt if your father could have given you the life your uncle has. It's not going to be easy to find you a husband to match up.'

'I don't want a husband!' Helen was indignant, but Angela wasn't listening to her.

'How far is it to Manchester?' she asked, getting up from her chair. 'I think we'll begin this afternoon. I'm sure we can do better than what you're wearing.'

And so here they were in Manchester, thought Helen wearily, dreading the afternoon ahead. Clothes had never interested her, beyond a natural desire to wear something in which she felt comfortable. Jeans had always provided that comfort, and the prospect of buying more feminine attire had no appeal whatsoever.

Miles dropped them in Piccadilly, with the arrangement that he should pick them up again in three hours. The young man looked sympathetically at Helen as Angela shepherded her out of the vehicle, and Helen reflected that she would rather spend the afternoon fighting off Miles' advances than trail around fashion shops with Angela.

One of the larger department stores had a teenage department, and Angela made straight for this, cringing rather affectedly at the raucous sound of music that emanated from that section. She turned her nose up, too, at the collection of gaudy garments hung out for display, and although Helen liked one or two of the drop-waisted dresses, she didn't offer any objections when Angela turned them down.

'You don't want to look like a tart, do you?' she demanded, marching out of the store, and Helen shrugged her shoulders, not really caring, one way or the other.

By the end of two hours Helen had various items of apparel to her credit. To give Angela her due, she did have good taste when it came to clothes, and the couple of dresses, the brown suede skirt suit, and the simple caftan for evening wear did bear the mark of style and expert tailoring. She found fault with anything Helen chose, even if it was something simple like a shirt or a sweater. She insisted that the girl left everything to her, and although her head was spinning after trying on so many discarded items, Helen was satisfied that Heath would approve of Angela's choice.

It was while they were enjoying a cup of tea in a café in the shopping precinct that Angela saw the hair salon. 'The final touch,' she declared, shunning Helen's suggestion that her hair should wait for another day. 'You want your uncle to be proud of you, don't you? Come along, then. We don't have that much time.'

The stylist who attended to them was a man, or at least he looked more like a man than a woman. Nevertheless, he did have hennaed hair and he wore make-up, and his voice, when he addressed them, was not so much lower than Helen's own.

'You want the hair cutting, you say,' he declared, tipping Helen's face from side to side and chewing on tinted lips. Helen had worn it loose to come to town, and she had to admit after trying on so many garments it did look more tumbled than usual. If only it was straight, she thought, like Angela's, then perhaps it would not look so bad. But it was wild and curly, and crinkly from the braid, and she reflected that to someone like this, it probably looked neglected.

'Well, I'll see what can be done,' he said at last, and Angela nodded.

'Good. I'll come back in about an hour. Don't worry about the payment. Just send the bill to Heathcliffe, Matlock Edge.'

'Matlock Edge,' repeated the man frowning. 'Ah, yes, I have heard of Mr Heathcliffe. Very well, madam, leave it to me. You can rely on Ricardo to do a good job.'

'Are you sure——' Helen began, half ready to suggest that perhaps they ought to consult Heath before embarking on something as momentous as cutting her hair, but Angela had gone. Content that she had done all that was required of her for the present, she was weaving her way down the precinct, too far away already to offer assistance.

'If you'll follow me . . .'

The man indicated that Helen should follow him into the larger salon at the back of the shop, and with a feeling of desperation, Helen obeyed. Could she ring Heath even now? Could she beg him to allow her to keep her hair the way she had always had it? But no, she didn't know where to contact him. And besides, he had already given his orders.

The sight of several other girls being attended to by other stylists was reassuring, but Helen couldn't forget that they were here by choice. She wasn't. She was being coerced by blackmail, and her chin jutted resentfully as she put all the blame on to Heath.

'Is something wrong?'

The man had seated her in an empty chair, and was presently assisting her to put on a salmon pink overall. 'Oh—no. No.' Helen met his reflected gaze in the mirror unhappily. 'It's just—well, I'm not sure about this, you see. I don't know whether I want my hair cut.'

The man smiled. 'Your mother was very certain.'

'My mother—oh! No, she's not my mother.' Helen coloured in amusement, wondering what Angela would have to say to that. 'She—er—she's just a—a friend of my uncle's, that's all. She thinks she knows what's best for me.'

'I see.' The man frowned and came round the side of the chair to look at her. 'Then let me show you something, will you? Wait here. I will not be a moment.' He lifted a hand. 'One moment, please.'

When he came back, he was carrying a dark wig, almost the same colour as Helen's hair. But unlike her hair, it was short and straight, exactly styled in the way Angela had directed.

'Give me a moment to secure your hair in a knot— so,' he declared, twisting her own hair into a corkscrew. 'Now, we slip the wig on like this. Just there. Now we see an impression of what your— uncle's friend is expecting.'

Helen gasped. Until that moment she had not realised how much hair contributed to a person's appearance. Shorn of the dancing mass of curls, her features looked different altogether, and she didn't like the alteration, she didn't like it at all.

'You see, your face is not thin and angular like your friend's,' explained Ricardo. 'Your features are fuller, younger; time enough for such severe styles when you are older. For now, I would suggest you allow me to trim the ends, to give the hair a little style, perhaps. To make it short would be sacrilege. It is beautiful hair. You should enjoy it.'

'Yes.'

Helen nodded, although she suspected he was actually saying that as she was more generously built than Angela, she needed all the help she could get. Remembering Angela's remarks at breakfast, she couldn't help but agree with him, viewing her own voluptuous curves with some distate. Nevertheless, if wearing her hair long assisted in distracting attention from her disadvantages, the last thing she should do was have it cut. With a sense of hurt indignation, she guessed Angela Patterson had known this, and her nails dug into her palms at the realisation that without

Ricardo's sensitivity, she could have ended up looking fat and frumpish.

When the older girl returned some fifty minutes later, Helen was seated in the waiting room, flicking through a magazine. She had never felt so relieved about anything in her life, and even Angela's burst of impatience could not disturb her.

'It has been cut, madam,' Ricardo averred, in answer to her irate enquiry. 'But the young lady did not wish me to cut it short, and I had to agree. It would have been unsuitable.'

Angela's lips tightened. 'What have you done with it, then?'

'Oh, I have cut away the split ends, shortened it a little, so that it can be worn without becoming tangled, washed it, had it blown dry. A comprehensive job, I can assure you.'

'Don't you think it looks nice, Miss Patterson?' asked Helen politely, unable to resist the small dig, and Angela gave her a frosty look.

'For the moment,' she conceded, and Helen was aware of the threat in her voice. 'Come along now. Ormerod will be waiting.' Her eyes flicked back to Ricardo. 'I'll tell Mr Heathcliffe you'll be sending your bill.'

Ricardo inclined his head, apparently unperturbed by the implied criticism, but as Helen followed Angela out of the salon, her nerves were taut. Once again she was remembering what Heath had said that morning, and she prayed that her recalcitrance would not arouse his anger.

CHAPTER FOUR

HELEN was in bed when Heath came home. She couldn't see the lights of his car, but she could hear the sulky purr of its engine as he cruised round to the garage, and she wondered with a sense of bitterness who he had spent the evening with.

When she and Angela had arrived back at Matlock Edge late that afternoon she had learned that Mrs Gittens had had a phone call from Heath, saying would not back for dinner. His reason was a business meeting in Leeds, but Helen had heard that excuse before. Nevertheless, she did get a certain satisfaction out of witnessing Angela's disappointment when she came down to find only two places set at the table.

'Does your uncle often dine out?' she asked, adjusting the shoulder strap of the elegant black sheath she was wearing, and Helen shrugged.

'Sometimes,' she conceded, not prepared to admit how often Heath was absent from the dinner table, and Angela made an annoyed grimace as she resignedly took her place.

Helen had not bothered to dress up for the meal. In the blouse and skirt she had worn to go to Manchester, she felt drab and uninteresting, and aware of Angela's eyes upon her, she avoided eating any of the fattening foods Mrs Gittens put before her.

A spicy fish soup was followed by roast beef and Yorkshire pudding, but Helen avoided the roast potatoes, which were her favourite. She concentrated instead on the broccoli, carrots and runner beans that accompanied them, drawing a troubled comment from Mrs Gittens when she came to clear the plates.

'What's the matter, lass?' she demanded. Are you sickening for something? It's not like you to be off your food, and I remember well you didn't eat your eggs this morning.'

Helen avoided Angela's eyes. 'I ate lunch, didn't I?'

'Lunch was salad,' declared Mrs Gittens. 'Rabbit's food. A young lass can't survive on lettuce and green beans. Come on now, Cook's made a rhubarb crumble for dessert. You'll enjoy that, won't you?'

Helen's mouth watered. 'Could I just have cheese and crackers?' she asked uncomfortably. 'Honestly, Mrs Gittens, I'm not hungry. I'll have some fruit later on, but it's too hot to eat stodgy puddings.'

'Huh!' Mrs Gittens plainly didn't believe her, and it didn't help to feel Angela Patterson's knowing eyes scorning her efforts. She couldn't wait for Mrs Gittens to leave the room to mock the younger girl's insistence, allowing her hand to slide suggestively over her slender figure with real enjoyment.

'So you've taken my words to heart,' she remarked, cradling her wine glass between her two palms and surveying Helen over the rim. 'Not before time, I'd say.'

'I knew you would,' responded Helen tensely, wishing she could tell her how she really felt, and Angela allowed a derisive laugh to escape her.

'I've never had a problem with my weight,' she declared smugly. 'I've been a size ten since I was sixteen. Being a size fourteen can be so limiting. So many of the most attractive garments aren't made in the larger sizes.'

'I wouldn't exactly call a size fourteen large!' retorted Helen, despising herself for arguing, but indignant at Angela's deliberate attempt to provoke her. 'Mrs Gittens in a size twenty, and I know friends of·mine who have to buy size sixteen in pants.'

Angela's lips twisted. 'Suit yourself. But you have to

admit, designers do tend to favour the slimmer figure. Don't worry about it. You can't help it. Some of us just have a fatty problem.'

'I don't have a fatty problem!' exclaimed Helen, unable to prevent the angry retort. 'My skin's clear, and I never get pimples!'

Angela smiled. 'Then why are you dieting?' she asked, in silken tones, and Helen had no polite response to give her.

Now, lying in bed, listening to the steady drone of Heath's motor, Helen wished she dared get out of bed and go and meet him, as she used to when she was younger. Often on nights when she couldn't sleep, she had tiptoed down the stairs at the sound of the front door closing, giggling conspiratorially when Heath raised his fingers to his lips. But since the incident at the pool, she had not attempted to leave her room, and she kicked the sheet aside frustratedly at the realisation that those days were gone for ever.

Unwanted, the memory of what had happened that morning returned to torment her. Heath had been so angry, she reflected miserably. He had acted as if it had all been her fault, and yet when he had kissed her, she had been unable to free herself, even had she wanted to. It was as if he had wanted to punish her, and punish himself at the same time, but inexperienced as she was, she knew it had all got out of his control. She touched her lips tentatively, aware of a certain sensual enjoyment when she did so. It was strange—in the past two days she had received two very different kinds of kisses, but she knew instinctively that in spite of Miles' aggression, Heath's had been the most dangerous.

A hollow thud announced the closing of the outer door, and Helen listened tensely for Heath's footsteps up the stairs. Although Matlock Edge was a large house, the stairs were old, and years of experience had alerted her to their every creak. He didn't come upstairs immediately, and she guessed he had gone into the kitchen to get himself a drink of milk. She used to share that drink with him, perched on a corner of the kitchen table, eyes sparkling at the unexpected treat . . .

With a dejected sniff, Helen rolled over on to her stomach, uncaring that the absence of the sheet meant that her buttocks were exposed to the air. It was too hot to wear a nightdress, even if Mrs Gittens did cluck reprovingly about young ladies and modesty, and she buried her face in the pillow, wishing she could sleep.

The sound of Heath's footsteps coming along the corridor caused her to shuffle a little more determinedly against the pillow, and then she froze into immobility when her door was suddenly opened. A shaft of light from the hall outside cast its brief illumination across the bed, and her breathing almost stopped. But then the light disappeared, the door closed again, and she expelled her breath weakly at the realisation that he had gone.

The next morning, it all seemed like a dream, but she knew it wasn't, rationalising what had happened with the realisation that Heath had probably looked in on her hundreds of times over the past fourteen years. After all, she was generally asleep when he came home, and she only hoped he thought that last night, and did not bring up the embarrassing subject of her nudity. It was already a bone of contention between them, and she could imagine the mileage Angela Patterson would get from such a juicy piece of gossip.

Nevertheless, she couldn't prevent the wave of colour that swept up her cheeks when he came into the morning room to find her already at the breakfast table, and it didn't help when he seated himself opposite her and regarded her with quiet intensity.

'I'm sorry,' he said, startling her still further, and

she looked up at him quickly, before resuming her concentration on the slice of toast on her plate.

'Sorry?' she mumbled, helping herself to marmalade. 'I don't know what you mean. You're often late for breakfast. As you can see, Miss Patterson hasn't even put in an appearance yet.'

'I wasn't talking about breakfast, and you know it,' he declared heavily. 'Helen, stop pretending you're going to eat that slice of bread! You've already spread two lots of marmalade on it, and it looks positively revolting. Just put your knife down and look at me. I promise it won't hurt at all.'

Helen wiped her fingers on her napkin without speaking, then unwillingly lifted her chin. 'I didn't know you were going to come into my room,' she muttered uncomfortably. 'It was such a hot night, I couldn't get to sleep with the covers on.'

Heath's thick lashes narrowed the green eyes. 'You were awake last night?'

Helen sighed. 'Yes.'

'You didn't say anything.'

Helen caught her breath. 'No.' She moved her shoulders helplessly. 'What would you have had me say? *Goodnight, Heath?*'

'Why not?'

'Why not?' Helen shook her head. 'And I suppose you would have done the same.'

'What do you mean?'

'I mean, if I'd come into your bedroom and found you in the raw, you'd have just said goodnight, just like that!'

Heath bent his head. 'We're not talking about me.'

'No.' Helen sounded bitter.

'We're not even talking about last night,' he added flatly. 'It was what happened yesterday morning I was apologising for. I'm sorry. After reflection, I realise it was my fault, not yours.'

Helen expelled her breath weakly. 'It was nobody's *fault*! I know I'm not the first girl you've kissed; and I don't expect I'll be the last.'

Heath stifled an oath. 'Helen, you're not a girl like that. Not just *any* girl. You're my niece.' He thrust a piece of cutlery savagely aside. 'I want thrashing, not you.'

Helen moistened her lips uncertainly. 'Heath, we're not related——'

His green eyes flashed. 'Aren't we?'

'You know what I mean.'

'I know what you're saying,' he amended grimly. 'However, I consider you are my niece, Helen. Anything else would be totally unacceptable.' He uttered a harsh laugh. 'Can you imagine what my mother would say if I told her what had happened?'

Helen's nails dug into the damask tablecloth. 'Well, I'm not sorry,' she declared tensely, looking away from his brooding air of hostility, and Heath thrust back his chair in angry rejection.

'Then you should be,' he exclaimed bleakly. 'I can only assume this relationship you've been having with young Ormerod has given you a taste for melodrama. Just don't try your wiles on me, Helen. I may still change my mind about that finishing school.'

'Oh, stop threatening me with that!' Helen burst out heatedly. 'It's not fair. Everything I say, everything I do, you're always holding that over my head. If you want to send me to Geneva, then send me. It's getting to the point when I don't care any more. Just stop giving me ultimatums!'

Heath's mouth compressed. 'Do you mean that?' he asked tersely, and Helen's balloon of confidence exploded.

'Yes! No! I don't know,' she answered unsteadily. 'Oh, leave me alone, can't you? I can't think straight any more.'

'As you wish.'

Heath would have left the room then, but the appearance of Mrs Gittens with a fresh pot of coffee forestalled him. 'Here we are,' she said busily. 'Your bacon and kidneys are on the way. Are you sure you wouldn't like some orange juice as well? Or maybe some cornflakes with strawberries?'

Helen's eyes widened. It was obvious from Mrs Gittens' conversation that Heath had spoken to her before coming to the morning room, and she sighed in unwilling relief that he was not going to leave her on such a sour note.

'Just the kidneys and bacon,' Heath was saying now, reluctantly resuming his seat and pouring himself a cup of the aromatic brew Mrs Gittens had provided, and the housekeeper turned reprovingly to Helen.

'And how about you?' she asked, tutting at the uneaten slice of toast on her plate. 'I don't know what's wrong with you, I really don't. Off your food yesterday, and scarcely touching a bite this morning!' She shook her head. 'I've told your uncle. I said to him, I didn't know what was the matter with you. Never known you to refuse good food in the past. Always had a healthy appetite, in my experience.'

Helen exchanged a puzzled look with Heath. Was that why he had apologised? she wondered. Had Mrs Gittens' concern about her loss of appetite led him to believe she was fretting over their encounter? With a feeling of frustration, Helen pushed the plate of toast aside and turned determinedly to the housekeeper. 'I've changed my mind,' she said. 'I will have some kidneys and bacon, after all!' and then felt her cheeks turn scarlet, as Angela Patterson sauntered into the room.

Helen didn't enjoy her moment of victory. Indeed, when the kidneys and bacon arrived, she had the greatest difficulty in doing justice to them, with both

Heath and Angela looking on. But at least she had disconcerted *him*, she thought afterwards, and it had been worth Angela's scornful observation to know that Heath had been thwarted.

Nevertheless, she waited a little tensely for Angela to tell her employer about their visit to Manchester the day before, but apart from saying that they had done a little shopping, Angela was surprisingly reticent. Perhaps she didn't want to get her into trouble, mused Helen doubtfully, but such a consideration did not seem characteristic.

After breakfast, Heath excused himself, and once again Helen was left to entertain Angela. 'I think we'll spend the morning in the garden,' Angela decided, looking with some satisfaction at the weather. 'It will give us time to talk, like we did yesterday. I want to know all about your friends and relations.'

'Wouldn't you like to play tennis?' suggested Helen, feeling bound to be civil after Angela's behaviour, but the other girl shook her head.

'Tennis is too strenuous,' she exclaimed. 'We'd get all hot and sweaty. It's not at all the occupation for a hot day. No, we'll sit by the pool, as I said. Just give me time to go and change into my swimsuit.'

Left alone, Helen hunched her shoulders uneasily. She wouldn't have minded a game of tennis. It would have helped to work off the huge breakfast she had just consumed. She knew Angela only wanted to pump her about her uncle really; about his friends and relations, not hers; and while sunbathing by the pool sounded appealing, talking about Heath right now did not.

On impulse, she left the house through the french doors on to the patio, and circled round to the garages. As usual Miles was there, his head tucked inside the bonnet of the Land Rover, but he turned at the sound of her footsteps and grinned when he saw who it was.

'Hi,' he said, lifting an oily hand, and Helen nodded a greeting.

'Hi,' she answered, going towards the garage that housed the Honda. 'Don't let me interrupt you. I just feel like some fresh air. If anyone comes looking for me, tell them I've gone for a ride, will you?'

'Is anyone likely?'

She grimaced. 'Maybe.'

'Heath?'

'I don't know. He's gone to the mill, hasn't he? His car's not here.'

'Oh, sure,' Miles made the concession. 'He left about half an hour ago. I thought you were supposed to be looking after the blonde bombshell.'

Helen shrugged. 'Is that what you call her?'

'It's what old Arnold called her,' Miles grinned. 'You must admit, she is dishy.'

'I'm glad you think so.' Helen realised she sounded bitchy, but she couldn't help it, and Miles made the wrong interpretation.

'Don't worry,' he said. 'I like my women with a bit more flesh upon their bones. And I like brunettes, too, particularly ones who are bouncing with sex-appeal!'

Helen wheeled the motorbike out of the garage and swung her leg across the saddle. 'Heath's not still mad at you, is he?' she asked, suppressing the impulse to tell him she didn't care about his opinion, and Miles shrugged his shoulders.

'I guess not. He doesn't exactly enthuse over my presence, if you know what I mean, but he's civil.' He sighed. 'For heaven's sake, it's not as if he hasn't known what's been going on.'

Helen frowned, pausing in the act of starting the engine. 'What has been going on?' she asked, arching her dark brows, and Miles cast his eyes heavenward, as if praying for tolerance.

'Come on, Helen,' he exclaimed, wiping his hands

on a rag he had pulled out of his overalls' pocket. 'You know. We've been pretty close since you came back from school.'

'We're friends, if that's what you mean,' retorted Helen shortly, not liking his attitude, and Miles came towards her, shaking his head.

'Oh, is that all?' he countered, covering the space between them, and not liking the look in his eyes, Helen stood on the starter. To her relief it fired at the first attempt, and before Miles could prevent her, she had skidded out of the yard and across the gravel path. By the time he reached the corner of the building, she was speeding down the drive towards the gates, and in her rear-view mirror she saw him turn away, a scowl upon his face.

To Helen's relief, Heath did not return at lunchtime, and when she came down to the dining room, newly showered and changed after her morning spent outdoors, Angela was already at the table.

'Where have you been?' she demanded, her feathers evidently ruffled by the girl's disappearance, and Helen decided to tell the truth rather than make up some elaborate story.

'I rode over to the farm,' she admitted, helping herself to a slice of melon, and Angela's lips thinned.

'Rode?' she echoed. 'On horseback, you mean?'

'No. Motorbike,' replied Helen cheerfully. 'Heath bought me a Honda for my sixteenth birthday. It's only a small machine, but Miles has fixed it so it really can accelerate.'

'Miles? Oh, you mean Ormerod,' concluded Angela scornfully. 'The young man your uncle found you fooling around with the day I arrived. He told me about him. He's one of the reasons I'm here to chaperone you.'

Helen's face flushed angrily. 'Heath told you that?'

'Of course.' Angela broke open a fresh roll with slender fingers. 'He had to give some reason for your disappearance immediately after my arrival. I must admit I don't admire your taste. A garage mechanic—honestly! Doesn't he have dirty fingernails?'

Helen was seething, as much with the realisation that Heath had discussed her affairs with Angela, as with Angela's remarks themselves. But Angela was here, and Heath wasn't, and Helen lost her temper.

'At least he knows what it is to do a decent job of work,' she flared. 'He's not a parasite—living off other people!'

'As you do,' put in Angela maliciously, savouring the taste of the fruit. 'Haven't you been living off your uncle, as you call it, ever since your parents were killed?'

Helen's throat hurt. 'That's not fair!'

'Why isn't it fair?' Angela arched her pencilled brows mockingly. 'Your uncle invited me here to do a job of work, as he saw it. He's not paying me for living off him.' She uttered an infuriating laugh. 'What are you suggesting, Helen?'

'You're not related to him!' retorted Helen painfully, and then put her fork aside as the obvious rejoinder occurred to her. *Nor was she*, though thank goodness Angela didn't mention that, but that didn't stop her from wondering exactly how accurate the other girl's assessment might be.

The sudden ringing of the telephone in another part of the house was a welcome diversion, and Helen looked over her shoulder anxiously, praying that it might be for her. It was. Mrs Gittens' appearance in the doorway, and her impatient comment that he ought to know better than to ring at mealtimes, had Helen instantly out of her chair, and she hurried across the hall to where the lifted receiver was lying. 'Heath?' she said huskily, unaware until that moment how badly she had wanted to hear his voice. 'Oh, Heath, I'm so glad it's you!'

'Why? What have you done?' Heath's tone was mildly tolerant, and Helen breathed a sigh.

'I've not *done* anything,' she exclaimed. 'I just wanted to talk to you, that's all. Is that so amazing? We don't talk much any more.'

'Have you been crying?' demanded Heath suspiciously, detecting the uneven tremor in her voice. 'Hell, what has Angela been saying to you now? Can't I leave you alone for five minutes without you two getting at one another's throats?'

'We're not—at least, it wasn't anything Miss Patterson said,' declared Helen doggedly. 'I—why are you ringing, Heath? Are you going to be out for dinner again?'

'No,' Heath responded abruptly, and then more evenly: 'Helen, you might as well tell me what's wrong. We may not get a chance to talk this evening.'

'Why not?'

'Because we're having company, that's why not,' replied Heath shortly. 'I've invited Greg Marsden and his wife for the weekend. He's going to Germany on Monday, as I believe I told you, and I want to make sure he's properly briefed before he leaves.'

Helen caught her lower lip between her teeth. 'Are Mark and Emma coming, too?' Mark and Emma were the Marsdens' fifteen-year-old twins, and Helen always enjoyed their uninhibited company.

'I'm afraid not.' Heath doused her sudden surge of enthusiasm. 'They're staying in Devon at present, with their grandmother, but you can invite some of your friends over for Sunday brunch, if you have a mind for it.'

'Thanks.' Helen sounded as disappointed as she felt. 'But most of my friends are away right now. It is July, Heath. Most people go on holiday in July and August.'

Heath sighed. 'You know I've told you I'll try and get away in September.'

'You promise?'

'I promise.'

'Just the two of us?'

'Oh, I don't know about that.'

'Why not?' Helen's cry was desperate. 'Last year we didn't get away at all, and you promised faithfully we'd have a holiday this summer!'

'I don't remember saying anything about us going alone,' retorted Heath flatly. 'It wouldn't be suitable, would it? I mean, you can imagine what people would think.'

Helen moistened her lips. 'Does that matter?'

'Yes, of course it matters.'

'It's never bothered you before.'

'You've never been seventeen before.'

'So from now on we're not to spend any time alone together?'

Heath expelled his breath impatiently. 'I didn't say that. But in any case, another year you'll probably want to spend your holidays with someone of your own age. You could have gone to St Moritz with the Kesslers last Christmas, if you hadn't been so stubborn. And even at Easter, you had the chance to go to Barbados.'

'Without you,' exclaimed Helen tautly, and heard the low oath Heath tried to stifle.

'Of course without me,' he agreed crisply. 'Helen, you're seventeen! You've got to break away some time.'

She caught her breath. 'Would you rather I got a job?'

'A job?' Heath sounded blank now. 'What has a job got to do with anything?'

'Just answer the question. Would you prefer it if I started to earn some money to support myself?'

'What?' Heath swore again. 'Helen, what's got into you? What do you want money for? Don't I give you a big enough allowance, is that it? Do you want a raise?'

'No!' Helen sniffed. 'Oh, it doesn't matter——'

'Like hell it doesn't.' She had his full attention now. 'Helen, do you want to get a job, is that it? Are you trying to tell me you want to be independent?'

'No.' Helen glanced over her shoulder anxiously, half afraid Angela Patterson had come to listen in to their conversation. 'We'll talk about it some other time, Heath. I'll tell Mrs Gittens to get a room prepared for the Marsdens, shall I?'

Heath was silent for a moment, and then he agreed. 'You do that,' he conceded tersely, and she rang off abruptly before he could say anything else.

'We're having company this weekend,' she told Angela offhandedly, when she returned to the dining room. She had already given Mrs Gittens the news, and although she was loath to do so, she knew Angela had to be told, too.

'Oh, who?' the other girl asked with interest. 'Anyone I might know?'

'That depends whether you're interested in computers,' replied Helen shortly. 'It's Greg Marsden and his wife. He runs H.M. Technical.'

'I see.' Angela absorbed the information consideringly. 'And Mr Marsden is a business colleague of your uncle's?'

'They're partners in the company,' conceded Helen shortly. 'Would you pass me the salt?'

'I thought your uncle's interests were all in wool,' ventured Angela, handing over the item requested, and Helen sighed.

'Well, they're not,' she retorted, looking down at the mixed salad on her plate without enthusiasm. There was a delicious quiche residing in the middle of the table, but she had purposefully avoided that. Now, however, she viewed the lettuce and tomato with little appetite, wishing she had never paid any attention to Angela's remarks about counting calories.

'Tell me, does your uncle travel much in the course of his work?' the older girl enquired now, and Helen controlled her sense of impatience.

'It's not important, is it?' she asked, meeting her gaze with cool determination, but Angela was not deterred.

'I'm intrigued, that's all,' she declared smoothly, deliberately helping herself to a large slice of the ham and egg flan. 'Daddy and I spent quite a lot of time out of the country when he was alive.' She paused and then continued: 'He was an archaeologist, you know—terribly interested in ancient civilisations, all that sort of thing. He knew Egypt intimately, and one of my earliest memories is of standing at the foot of the Great Pyramid wondering——'

'I thought you said your father was a writer,' Helen interrupted her frowning. 'You told Heath——'

'Oh, well, yes, he was,' Angela quickly amended her story. 'He wrote about archaeology, of course. I did tell you his books were rather technical, didn't I?'

'You also said your father moved away from London because he needed solitude for his writing,' Helen reminded her shortly. 'You said you moved to Cornwall. Was that before or after you went to Egypt?'

'Well, afterwards naturally.' Angela's smile was frosty. 'Just because one lives in Cornwall it doesn't mean one is necessarily cut off from the rest of the world.'

'I suppose not,' Helen conceded the point.

'I suppose you've travelled with your uncle,' Angela added resentfully, and Helen shrugged.

'Some,' she agreed. 'But not usually when he's on business,' and Angela's nostrils flared at the carefully spoken evasion.

CHAPTER FIVE

HELEN was sitting disconsolately by the swimming pool when Heath and his guests arrived. They turned up in separate cars: Heath driving his own Porsche, and Greg Marsden broad and expansive behind the wheel of his Volvo estate. Helen heard the individual engines as she was dipping the toes of one foot into the water, and her nerves tightened familiarly at the sound of Heath's voice. She expected Mrs Gittens would meet them, and show the Marsdens to their rooms, but because it was such a beautiful afternoon, Heath escorted his guests along the path by the orchard, and Helen was caught in the process of scrambling hastily to her feet.

'Well, well!' Greg Marsden's booming tones matched his appearance. Tall and broad, the evidence of his success bulging carelessly over his waistline, he looked years older than his business partner, but his manner was jovial, and infinitely more friendly, thought Helen, glancing away from her uncle's dark face. 'What have we here? You didn't tell me you had other guests, Heath.'

'Stop teasing, Greg!' Marion Marsden smiled sympathetically at Helen. 'How are you, love? I must say you're more grown-up every time I see you.'

Helen smiled rather nervously, aware of the brevity of the bikini and Angela's opinion of it, but Greg did not allow his wife to have the last word. 'Isn't that what I'm saying?' he demanded, patting Heath heavily on the shoulder. 'Your niece is quite a young lady, isn't she, old man? The last time I saw her she was still in a gymslip.'

'The last time you saw her was at Easter,' replied

66

his wife firmly. 'And she wasn't wearing a gymslip then. Don't run away, Helen. Don't let this big idiot of mine embarrass you. Stay and have tea with us.'

'Oh, really, I——' Helen broke off awkwardly, wishing she had anticipated Heath might bring his guests this way and that she had had time to get dressed before this meeting. Heath had said nothing so far; just looked at her as if he thought she had engineered this encounter, and the memory of that other occasion by the pool was too close to dismiss.

'Where's Miss Patterson?' Heath asked now, breaking the uneasy silence between them, and Helen moistened her lips before replying.

'She—er—she went to get changed,' she offered, perching rather edgily on the arm of a cushioned lounger. 'I really think I should get changed, too.'

'Why?' Greg lowered his weight into the lounger beside her, grinning up at her irrepressibly. 'Why deny a poor harassed businessman the chance to dream? You're not cold, are you? It's a perfectly marvellous afternoon. Come on, Helen. Relax. Heath, go ask that housekeeper of yours if she's got a nice can of lager residing in the fridge.'

Heath slung the jacket he had been carrying over one shoulder and unbuttoned the collar of his shirt. Watching him, Helen wasn't at all sure what he wanted her to do, but somehow she sensed, rather than guessed, that he was not happy with the present arrangement.

'I'll tell her,' she said, getting to her feet. 'I'll tell Mrs Gittens you'd like a beer, Mr Marsden.' And before any of them could stop her, she hurried away through the french doors into the morning room.

Mrs Gittens was in the kitchen with Cook as Helen had expected, preparing a tray to bring out. 'Is it tea they want?' she asked, as Helen came through the swing door, and the girl drew a deep breath before explaining. 'So—beer for one. And how about your uncle?'

'I'll take tea, Mrs Gittens, thank you.' Heath's low attractive tones brought Helen round with a start. 'If you'll serve it on the patio, I'll be very grateful.'

'Of course,' Mrs Gittens smiled, and with an apologetic grimace, Helen made her retreat. But in the corridor outside the kitchen, Heath's voice arrested her, and she turned back reluctantly to find him striding after her.

'Wait,' he said severely, reaching her in a few paces. 'Come into the library. I want to have a word with you.'

'Can't it wait?' Helen looked down pointedly at her swimsuit and bare feet, but Heath shook his head.

'We may not have an opportunity later,' he essayed, going ahead of her and pushing open the leather-studded door. 'Go on. Don't look at me like that. The Marsdens will wonder what's going on, if I don't go back and join them soon.'

She sighed, stepping across the thickly carpeted floor on slightly uncertain legs. She was selfconscious with Heath now, as she had never been selfconscious before, and her body reacted by thrusting hardened nipples against the thin cotton cloth. Sinking into one of the green leather armchairs, she tried to disguise the provocative evidence of her arousal, but Heath came round the chair to face her, and she knew from his hardening expression that he was not unaware of her body's betrayal. But he made no comment, merely adjusted his eyes to the level of hers, whether or not she could sustain that intent appraisal.

'Why did you ask me on the phone whether I wished you to find a job?' he asked, propping his lean hips against the rim of the table behind him, his voice cool and expressionless. 'Have I ever given you the impression that I was unhappy with your financial situation?'

'N—o——'

Helen drew the word out, and before she could add anything more, Heath went on: 'Then has Angela insinuated that an occupation of some sort might help to solve your problems?'

'No—o——'

Once again Helen made a negative response, her eyes sliding away from his, and he ran an impatient hand under his collar, as if the heat of the day was not aiding his temper. 'So why suggest such a thing?' he demanded sharply. 'Aren't you happy here?'

Helen looked at him then, her eyes mirroring her indignation. 'Do you have to ask that?'

He shrugged. 'I'm just trying to make sense of a conversation we had just a few hours ago,' he retorted flatly. 'There has to have been some reason for you to ask that question. I'm just trying to find out what that reason was.'

Helen moved her shoulders now. 'I expect I was just making conversation,' she declared carelessly. 'Is that all? Can I go and dress now?'

His mouth compressed. 'When did you get that—that thing you're wearing?'

She bent her head. 'I don't remember. Last year—the year before——'

'Burn it,' said Heath harshly. 'I don't want to see you wearing it again. It's not decent. Get Miss Patterson to add bathing suits to the list of items you require. I presume you have got something decent to wear this evening.'

Helen got to her feet. 'I won't disgrace you, if that's what you mean.'

'For God's sake!' He straightened away from the desk. 'What's the matter with you, Helen? For the last few days—ever since Miss Patterson came to Matlock, in fact—you've been acting completely out of character. Disobedience I can understand; temper tantrums I can understand; what I can't understand is this sudden urge you have to make me feel like a bastard!'

Helen's eyes widened. 'Is that how I make you feel?'

He drew in his lips. 'I want you to stop all this nonsense about jobs and worrying over our relationship and start behaving like the young woman you are becoming. Marion's right—you are growing up. And with Angela's help, who knows, you may find yourself a husband before the year is out.'

Helen caught her breath. 'Is that what you want?' she demanded accusingly. 'Is that why you've brought Angela Patterson here? To get me off your hands?'

'Oh, for heaven's sake!' Heath raised his eyes heavenward. 'Stop taking everything so seriously. Finding a husband is not something I'm threatening you with. Good God, most girls are looking for someone to marry from the minute they realise what the opposite sex is!'

'Not me!'

'What do you mean—not you?' Heath drew a deep breath. 'You're not old enough yet to know what you want.'

'I don't want to get married!' declared Helen unsteadily. 'I know that.'

'Why not, for God's sake?'

'You're not married.'

'I'm different.'

'No, you're not. You need women. Mrs Gittens said so.'

'Oh, did she?' Heath's eyes darkened. 'And what else has Mrs Gittens been saying?'

'Oh, nothing.' She shifted uncomfortably, realising her reckless words could cause the old housekeeper some embarrassment. 'She wasn't talking about you. It was just something I—I overheard.'

'Really?'

'Yes, really.' She looked up at him helplessly, more than ever at a disadvantage without shoes. 'Honestly, Heath, you've got to believe me. I'd hate you to confront Mrs Gittens with something like that. She'd die, she would, honestly!'

'Isn't it the truth, then?' Heath took the step that brought him closer to her, his eyes glinting dangerously, and Helen gasped.

'I'm not lying, if that's what you mean.'

'So she did say it?'

'Yes. No.' Helen shook her head. 'Oh, you're just doing this to confuse me! You don't really care what Mrs Gittens says about you. You don't care what anybody says about you.'

'I wouldn't say that.'

'I would.' She hunched her shoulders. 'Can I go now, *please*?'

Heath shrugged. 'I suppose you'd better.'

'Thanks.'

She made for the door, but he was swifter, reaching past her to turn the handle for her, his green eyes mocking as they surveyed her confusion. 'Don't hate me, Helen,' he said, surprisingly, and her face flamed with sudden colour.

'I don't hate you,' she exclaimed, but he deliberately inclined his head.

'You could—very easily,' he essayed, his warm breath fanning her bare shoulder, and her breathing was laboured as she ran up the stairs to her room.

Marion Marsden came to Helen's room when she was getting ready for dinner. 'I'm not intruding, am I?' she asked doubtfully, when she saw Helen was still in her dressing gown, and the girl quickly shook her head.

'Of course not. Come in,' she invited, stepping aside. 'You can help me to decide what to wear.'

Marion entered the bedroom, surveying its ample proportions with renewed admiration. 'This really is a lovely room, Helen,' she declared, spreading her arms expressively. 'You'll miss it when you get married. There aren't too many houses like Matlock around.'

Helen moved her shoulders half impatiently as she closed the door. 'Why is everybody talking about marriage all of a sudden?' she exclaimed. 'I don't expect I'll get married—at least, not for ages anyway.'

'Who else has been talking about marriage?' enquired Marion innocently, seating herself on the edge of the bed, but Helen was not prepared to tell her.

'You look nice,' she said instead, changing the subject. 'That shade of pink becomes you. I just wish I knew what I was going to wear.'

Marion tilted her head to glimpse her reflection in the mirrors of the dressing table and then sighed. 'I'm going grey!' she said, touching her cap of light brown curls resignedly. 'Be thankful you don't have to worry about things like extra inches and unbleached roots!'

'I wouldn't say that,' Helen sighed. 'Miss Patterson thinks I'm overweight.'

'Miss Patterson? Oh, you mean this woman Heath's employed to look after you?' Put like that it didn't sound half so intimidating, Helen realised in amazement. 'I met her at tea. I shouldn't worry about what she says. She's probably envious. After all, you have got everything going for you, haven't you?'

'Have I?'

Marion gave her an old-fashioned look. 'Stop fishing for compliments, Helen. You know you have. Now, what is it you're planning to wear?'

'No, really, Marion, I wasn't fishing for compliments, honestly.' Helen chewed unhappily at her lower lip. 'I just want you to be honest with me. Don't you think I'm—fat?'

Marion sighed. 'Of course not.'

'But I'm not slim, am I?'

Marion shook her head. 'You've got some shape, that's all. You're not *thin*, I'll grant you that, but you're certainly not fat. And with that hair . . .'

Helen swung round from the critical examination she had been giving herself in the wardrobe mirror. 'You don't think my hair needs cutting, then?'

'Cutting?' Marion snorted. 'Who gave you that idea? Not Heath, I'll bet.' She paused as the girl looked uncomfortable. 'Helen, your hair is one of your best features. You'd be mad to have it cut.'

Helen nodded. 'That's what I thought.'

'So—if you've finished admiring yourself . . .'

'I wasn't——' Helen coloured, and then saw Marion smiling at her and looked rueful. 'The dress,' she said determinedly. 'I'll show you what we bought.'

Under Marion's experienced eye, the two dresses and the caftan Angela had chosen were brought out for inspection. 'They are beautiful, aren't they?' murmured Helen wistfully, fingering the dark blue satin of a cap-sleeved dress with a scooped-out neckline, suitable for both day and evening wear. 'I like that one best,' she added, pointing to the other, a fine knitted silk, whose tubular shape accentuated every curve and sinew. 'It's really smooth, isn't it?'

'Yes.' Marion sounded less enthusiastic, turning from the dresses to survey Helen's youthful figure and then back again.

And as Helen watched her, her own enthusiasm faded. 'You see,' she declared, after a few moments, her confidence crumpling. 'You're doubtful whether they're going to fit me, aren't you? Why don't you admit it? I am fat, like Angela says.'

'You're not fat!' Marion spoke firmly. 'And the dresses are—beautiful, as you say. All I'm wondering is whether they're entirely suitable for a girl of your age.'

'What do you mean?'

'Helen, you're not that much older than Emma, and quite frankly, I wouldn't allow her to wear something like this.'

'Why not?'

'Why not?' Marion moistened her lips. 'Well, because they're for an older woman. Someone of your Miss Patterson's age, I'd imagine.'

Helen sighed. 'I'm not a child, you know, Marion.'

'I know. But you're not a sophisticated woman either. Where did you buy these things? Not in a teenage department, I'll bet.'

'We got them at Mallory's,' replied Helen defensively. 'I got a suit there, too.'

'Mallory's.' Marion shook her head. 'What's that? A dress shop in Bradford?'

'In Manchester, actually,' replied Helen tensely. 'Angela didn't like the teenage departments. She said the music was too loud and the clothes were cheap.'

'Well, so they are. Cheap, I mean. But that's because young people like a lot of clothes rather than one or two expensive items in their wardrobe. And in any case, there are establishments that sell *good* teenage clothes. Heath should have sent you down to me. I'd have kitted you out—and not in clothes more suited to a woman of my age, not yours.'

'Oh, Marion . . .' Helen hunched her shoulders. 'So what am I going to wear then? The caftan?'

'Not tonight,' replied Marion flatly. 'It's too warm.' She paused. 'Tell me, do you happen to have a skirt you could wear?'

'A skirt?' Helen's spirits drooped still further. 'Oh, not a skirt again!'

'So you do have a skirt,' Marion gauged accurately. 'Now, does Heath have a white shirt you could borrow? One with wide sleeves, for preference. Then I'll tell you what we're going to do.'

Helen gasped. 'How could I get a shirt of Heath's?'

'Ask Mrs Gittens,' advised Marion sagely. 'I'm sure she knows what Heath keeps in his dressing room better than he does. She'll get a shirt for you, if you ask her nicely. Now, hurry up. Do it. We don't have that much time.'

Twenty minutes later Helen surveyed her reflection with some disbelief. Who would have thought that a plain black skirt and a man's white shirt could look so attractive? she asked herself in amazement. And it was all due to Marion, and her instinctive eye for style.

The shirt Mrs Gittens had brought her was made of silk, but the housekeeper had made it known she did not approve of this clandestine use of her employer's belongings. 'What Mr Heathcliffe will say, I don't know,' she averred, refusing to respond to Helen's cajoling praise. 'I thought you and Miss Patterson bought some clothes that day you went to Manchester.'

'We did,' Helen admitted, unconsciously rubbing her cheek against the fine material. 'But Mrs Marsden thinks they might not be suitable, so she's going to help me to dress.'

'Huh!'

Mrs Gittens went away muttering to herself, but regarding her appearance now, Helen felt sure the old housekeeper would approve when she saw how Marion's plan had turned out. The plain white silk shirt was open at the neck to expose the creamy column of her throat. The hem of the shirt almost covered Helen's hips, but Marion had cinched it in at the waist, with a blue silk scarf of her own worn like a sash. The long sleeves hugged her wrists due to the addition of two carved silver bangles Heath had once brought her back from Morocco, and around her neck was a silver medallion, also borrowed from Marion for the occasion.

'Well? What do you think?' asked Marion now, touching the loose curls that tumbled in wild profusion over her shoulders. 'I think you'll agree, simple things dressed up with bits and pieces can prove quite attractive.'

'It's—it's great!' exclaimed Helen, turning impulsively to give the older woman a hug. 'I look—I look quite—quite——'

'—sexy, I know,' agreed Marion drily. 'Now, put on your sandals and let's go. We're already fifteen minutes late.'

Heath and his guests were having drinks on the patio when Helen and Marion came to join them. Angela was there, sleek and sophisticated as usual, in slinky black culottes worn with a matching strapless top, and Greg Marsden looked quite presentable this evening in a dark dinner jacket. Only Heath's attire gave any colour to the scene, his dark green velvet dinner jacket an attractive contrast to his cream ruffled shirt.

However, much to her dismay, it was Helen's appearance that attracted the most attention, and judging by Angela's expression, it was not to her advantage. Angela's lips parted in dismay when she saw the girl she had been brought here to chaperone, and her eyes turned swiftly to Marion Marsden, as if seeking an explanation.

Heath, conversely, showed no surprise at her style of dress, though his eyes did narrow slightly as he watched Greg Marsden's frank appraisal. It was as if he was judging the effect she was having on his guests, thought Helen half indignantly, and her colour rose accordingly to match her heated blood.

'I say, you look jolly dishy this evening, young Helen,' Greg exclaimed, breaking the pregnant silence which had heralded their appearance. 'What a pity there's no young man to appreciate it. You'll have to make do with me instead.'

Helen's smile was not forced. Greg could always be relied upon to keep the party moving, and shaking off the feelings of resentment Heath's attitude was arousing, she tried to equal his banter. 'You don't look so bad yourself,' she declared, ignoring the hostile looks Angela was casting in their direction. 'I always think a dinner jacket looks so well on a man.'

'It hides a multitude of sins,' remarked Marion drily, giving her husband a pointed dig in his stomach. 'Hmm, yes, Heath, I'd like a dry sherry, if you have one. How about you, Helen? What are you going to drink to celebrate your—independence?'

Helen looked nervously towards Heath as he poured Marion's sherry from a bottle placed on the trolley Mrs Gittens had wheeled out for them. 'I'm not sure,' she murmured, not usually interested in alcoholic drinks. 'Perhaps I'll have a sherry, too. Or maybe a dry Martini?'

'Sherry,' said Heath flatly, handing her a narrow glass. 'You may look like an adult, but you're still under age.'

'Don't be a spoilsport, Heath!' Greg came to tuck his hand beneath Helen's elbow. 'Hmm, you smell nice, too. What is that? Chanel Number Five?'

'It's Charlie, actually,' admitted Helen, with some amusement. 'I'm glad you like it. You and Marion bought it for me last Christmas.'

'And that serves you right,' declared Marion delightedly, laughing at her husband's rueful face. 'What time is dinner, Heath? I must admit this country air does wonders for my appetite.' She paused before adding deliberately: 'Don't you feel the same, Miss Patterson?'

Angela turned from her contemplation of the rose garden and looked coolly into the other woman's face. 'I don't have a large appetite at the best of times, Mrs Marsden. I'm lucky that way.'

'Oh, I wouldn't say that.' Marion spoke pleasantly enough. 'If you had a man's hearty appetite to satisfy every day, you might find your attitudes changing.'

'I doubt it.' Angela's smile was wintry. 'One should always try to control one's appetites, don't you agree?'

'It depends what appetites one's talking about,' remarked Greg irrepressibly. 'Haven't you ever had a man to cook for, Angela? You don't mind me calling you Angela, do you? That is what Heath calls you, isn't it?'

Angela forced a polite laugh. 'Of course. Call me Angela by all means. And in answer to your question, I cooked for a man for many years: my father.'

'Oh, shame!' Greg grimaced, and then, to Angela's evident relief, he turned to Heath once more and they began a discussion about the cost of fuel, leaving the three women free to make their own conversation.

'Wherever did you get that outfit from?' Angela demanded of Helen, the moment they were alone together. Marion had gone to admire the flowering shrubs Arnold Wesley had planted around the croquet lawn, and as the two men were occupied, Angela's words were not audible to anyone else.

'As a matter of fact, Marion suggested it,' replied Helen unwillingly. 'She thought it looked very nice, and so do I.'

'And what was wrong with one of those dresses we bought in Manchester?' Angela drew a deep breath. 'Can you imagine how embarrassed I'd have been tonight if anyone else had been present?'

'What do you mean?'

'Your uncle employed me to give you guidance about what to wear,' hissed Angela impatiently. 'I dread to think what his opinion is. I shall have to explain to him tomorrow that evidently you're not prepared to take one iota of notice of me!'

'The dresses we bought are too old for me,' muttered Helen in a low voice. 'Marion said——'

'*Marion* said!' echoed Angela scornfully. 'What does Marion know? That dress she's wearing was probably fashionable twenty years ago.'

'That's not fair!' Helen was indignant, but Angela only screwed up her nose.

'You can't believe Marion Marsden is any judge of style or fashion.'

'I like this,' declared Helen mutinously, looking down at the unbuttoned neckline of the shirt. 'It's— it's me.'

'Sloppy,' said Angela contemptuously. 'Exactly like you. But if that's the way you want to look——'

'Are you ready for dinner, Mr Heathcliffe?'

Mrs Gittens' homely voice provided a welcome intrusion, and Heath glanced round briefly at his guests before acknowledging that they were. 'Come along, Marion. The food's on the table,' exclaimed her husband incorrigibly, and Helen had to smile at Angela's hastily disguised frustration.

It was after the meal was over that Helen found herself alone with Heath for the first time that evening. Coffee was being served on the terrace as it was such a beautiful evening, but when she would have followed Angela and the Marsdens, his hand about her wrist detained her. The feel of his strong fingers circling her arm just below the broad silver bangle was disturbing, even through the fine silk, and Helen's pulses raced alarmingly as she anticipated a closer intimacy.

'I just wanted to say I applaud the improvement,' he commented quietly, his free hand flicking carelessly at the collar of her shirt. 'I shall compliment Angela in the morning. She's done a good job.'

Helen was so choked up, she didn't know how to respond and taking her silence for acquiescence, Heath abruptly let her go. 'You'd better join the others,' he said, a sudden harshness to his voice. 'I want to have a

word with Mrs Gittens. She really excelled herself this
evening, don't you think? The Chateaubriand was——'

'Angela didn't—I mean—I—I——'

'Not now, Helen.'

Heath was already striding across the hall in the
direction of the kitchen, and the indifference of his
dismissal made Helen's already bruised emotions
simmer. He didn't want to hear her explanation, she
thought indignantly. He was quite certain that Angela
had to be responsible for any improvement in her
appearance.

All right, Heath, she said to herself silently, you
know best. I just hope Angela appreciates your
confidence in her!

CHAPTER SIX

IT was late the following afternoon before Helen saw Heath again. On Saturday morning she was late for breakfast, and by the time she came down Heath and Greg were already closeted in the study. As the two men were unavailable, Marion suggested a shopping trip to Bradford, and although Angela was evidently not enthusiastic, she agreed to come along.

'Quite frankly, I'd as soon she stayed at home,' confessed Marion, seating herself beside Helen in the Mercedes. Then: 'Are you sure Heath lets you drive this? It's an expensive piece of machinery for you to be around.'

'Don't you trust me?' Helen smiled. 'No, honestly, I've driven this car since I first got my licence. I used to think Heath trusted me, too.'

'Used to think?' Marion's brows drew together. 'What's changed your mind?'

'Oh, this and that.' Helen didn't really want to discuss it. 'Where is Angela? We've been waiting for ten minutes.'

'Didn't Heath use to have a young man to drive you around?' Marion asked curiously. 'I seem to remember——'

'Miles Ormerod,' agreed Helen, interrupting her. 'Oh, Miles is still around. He just doesn't work weekends, that's all. Unless Heath asks him specially, I mean.'

'Didn't you use to have a crush on him?' murmured Marion innocently, and Helen's fingers tightened on the wheel.

'Who told you that?' she demanded. 'Heath, I

suppose. Well, you're wrong. Miles and I are just friends: *good* friends, as they say in all the best magazines.'

Marion shrugged. 'No need to get so heated about it, Helen. It's quite natural——'

'What's quite natural?' Helen turned to look at her accusingly. 'That I should fool around with Miles Ormerod?'

'Well, he is about your own age,' observed Marion mildly, 'and as I recall, he's quite a handsome young man.'

'So what?'

'Well, so girls of your age usually indulge in flirtations with the opposite sex.'

'Not me.'

'Why not you?' Marion sighed. 'I'm not suggesting you should consider marrying the young man——'

'Marrying? Marrying?' Helen gasped. 'Why does everything have to come back to marriage? I told you last night——'

'Oh, all right, Helen.' There was an edge to Marion's voice now, and Helen was contrite. She had not meant to be rude, but she reacted so strongly to any allegation that might mean she would have to leave Matlock Edge.

'I'm sorry,' she mumbled, just as Angela came elegantly out of the house, and Marion squeezed her arm reassuringly.

'It's okay,' she murmured, reaching for the seatbelt. 'I shouldn't have opened my big mouth. Heath will work things out his own way. He usually does.'

Helen objected to the suggestion that Heath might consider himself in command of her destiny. She wanted to control her own life. But with Angela Patterson climbing into the car at that moment, she could hardly voice her misgivings.

Bradford was busy with Saturday shoppers, and

after parking the car, they found it difficult to stay together. 'Why don't we split up and arrange to meet for lunch later?' Marion suggested, after waiting for several minutes for Angela to catch up. 'Where shall we have lunch, Helen? Do you know a good restaurant? If we agree to meet at one o'clock, we won't need to spend our time looking for one another.'

'I'm agreeable,' said Angela coolly, evidently relieved not to have to accompany Marion around the shops, and Helen's brow furrowed as she tried to come up with an answer.

'There's the Crown,' she said doubtfully. 'I know Heath sometimes eats there when he's entertaining business colleagues.'

'What could be better?' exclaimed Marion eagerly. 'We'll meet at the Crown at one o'clock. I suppose any of these people could tell us where it is?'

'It's just over there, in Villiers Street,' declared Helen at once, and Marion nodded comfortably.

'All right,' she said. 'One o'clock it is, Miss Patterson. Don't be late—I expect I'll be hungry!'

Angela's smile was thin as she sauntered away, and as soon as she had been swallowed up by the crowds, Marion breathed a sigh of relief.

'Thank goodness she's gone!' she declared, grasping Helen's arm securely. 'Come on now, lead me to the nearest coffee shop. I'm badly in need of a sticky cream cake!'

'You mean, you and I are not splitting up?' asked Helen, after they were installed in a nearby coffee house, with chocolate éclairs in front of them.

'Of course not.' Marion grimaced. 'I thought you and I might do a little shopping, and I didn't want Miss Patterson vetoing my suggestions.'

The teenage boutique attached to one of the larger stores did not look half so tawdry with Marion by her side. In the space of an hour, Marion had approved her choice of several items to add to her wardrobe, among them a button-through jacket and drawstring pants, a camisole dress, that was laced to the waist, and another dress of printed chiffon, with a scooped neck and dropped waist. She bought a couple of sweaters, too, and a pretty chamois skirt, and a silky suede jacket with fringing around the hem.

'I don't know what Heath will say,' Helen protested doubtfully, as they unloaded their parcels into the boot of the Mercedes before going to meet Angela for lunch.

'I'm quite sure Heath will approve of the way you look,' declared Marion firmly. 'He approved of you last night, didn't he?'

'Oh, yes.' Helen was tempted to tell Marion exactly what Heath had said, but instead she kept his comments to herself.

Although it had been a promising morning, the weather changed as they were having lunch, and when they emerged from the Crown it had started to rain. 'Let's go home,' suggested Marion, tilting her head up to the sky. 'This isn't going to give up, and I don't feel like getting soaked, do you?'

'Not particularly.' Helen looked at Angela. 'Is that all right with you?'

'Perfectly.' Angela wrinkled her nose as a spot of rain invaded her nostril, and shrugging her shoulders at Marion, Helen led the dash for the car.

Even in the rain, Matlock was beautiful, Helen thought contentedly, as she drove the powerful car along the private road through the park. The trees were dripping moisture on to the backs of the horses sheltering beneath their branches, but although the sky was grey, the pasture was green and lush with grass.

'You can imagine horse-drawn carriages coming along this path, can't you?' Marion reflected, almost echoing Helen's thoughts, and she smiled.

'Heath used to have an old phaeton in the stables,' she recalled reminiscently. 'It was pulled by two horses. I believe they were the fastest form of transport years ago.'

Marion arched her brows. 'What happened to it?'

'Oh——' Helen grimaced, 'I overturned it once in the park. Heath disposed of it after that.'

'I can imagine!' Marion was horrified. 'You could have been killed!'

'Yes, that's what he said.' Helen brought the car to a halt at the drive gates, and got out to open them. 'At any rate, I didn't get to drive it again,' she remarked, climbing in again to take the Mercedes through. 'I was confined to riding my pony after that.'

Heath and Greg Marsden were still working in the study when they got back to the house. Leaving Helen to unload the boot in private, Marion led the way into the house, and by the time Helen joined them in the sitting room, Mrs Gittens was fetching afternoon tea.

'Mr Heathcliffe said to tell you he'd like to talk to you before dinner, Miss Patterson,' the housekeeper declared, addressing herself to Angela, and Helen's mouth went dry. She could guess why Heath wanted to speak to her companion, and she was guiltily aware of her own duplicity. But he had not given her a chance to explain, she defended herself fiercely, and then changed her mind again when she considered how embarrassing it would be. Time healed all wounds, and the pleasure she had had in Marion's company and in buying so many pretty things had soothed her indignation. She couldn't let Heath make such a mistake. She would tell him the truth as soon as she had finished her tea.

Angela disappeared after sipping only half a cup of tea and refusing all offers of wafer-thin sandwiches or biscuits. 'She's gone to prepare for her interview,' remarked Marion dourly, helping herself to another smoked salmon delicacy. 'Do you get the feeling that Miss Patterson would like to be mistress here herself?'

'She wouldn't be the first,' declared Helen carelessly. 'Heath's been fighting off suitors for as long as I can remember. I don't think he even notices any more.'

'I wouldn't be too sure.' Marion poured herself more tea. 'He's not getting any younger, you know, Helen, and he's got to get married, sooner or later.'

Helen stiffened. 'Why?'

'Why?' Marion shook her head. 'You know why. He needs someone to leave all this to, doesn't he?'

'A son, you mean?'

'Or a daughter. I don't think the laws of primogeniture would matter too much to Heath. But he needs a wife to give him a child, doesn't he?'

Helen hunched her shoulders. 'He'd never marry anyone like Angela Patterson.'

'Why not?' Marion shrugged. 'Oh, I'll admit, she's not my cup of tea, but you and I can't judge what will appeal to Heath.'

Helen could feel her whole body growing tense as Marion spoke. It was ridiculous, of course. Heath couldn't be attracted to Angela Patterson. She was too cold, too bitter, too everything that Helen objected to most. Only she wasn't the one who was involved here, she realised. As Marion said, how could she judge the kind of woman Heath might find appealing? She had thought he liked her, she had thought he considered her his ideal. She had soon been abused of that contention, and he *had* brought Angela here on the flimsiest of pretexts. What if he really liked her? What if he had brought her here to see how she fitted in? How she and Helen got along together? Maybe that was why he got so mad when she was rude to Angela . . .

'Are you all right?'

Marion was looking at her strangely, and Helen quickly pulled herself together. 'Yes,' she exclaimed. 'Yes, of course. Why shouldn't I be?'

'I don't know.' Marion frowned. 'You've gone awfully pale, all of a sudden.'

'Don't be silly.' Helen got to her feet. 'I expect I was flushed from carrying all those things upstairs. I had to make two journeys.'

'Wait until Heath sees them,' remarked Marion sagely. 'At least he can't say that Angela taught you what to wear.'

'No,' Helen smoothed her damp palms down the seams of her skirt, 'he can't say that.' She edged towards the door. 'I'll see you later, Marion. I want to go and unpack.'

With the sitting room door closed, however, Helen did not make for the stairs. Instead she hurried along the corridor to Heath's study, pausing only a moment before knocking at the door.

'Later, Mrs Gittens.'

Heath's impatient tones were audible through the solid panels, but Helen knocked once again. If she went away now, she thought uneasily, she would not get another chance to speak to Heath before he spoke to Angela, and in spite of her dislike of the other girl, her conscience would not let her leave it be.

'I said later, Mrs Gitt——' Heath broke off abruptly as he swung open the door to find Helen outside. 'Oh, it's you,' he added, without enthusiasm. 'What do you want? Didn't Mrs Gittens tell you I'd be tied up until later?'

'Yes, she told me.' Helen had the greatest difficulty in keeping her tone polite when he spoke to her like that, even though she was aware of him with every fibre of her being. He had discarded his tie and his shirt was unbuttoned almost to his waist, and the warm male scent of his body was enhanced by the heat of the room behind him. Her fingers itched to touch him, even though she told herself it was crazy, and the smooth brown skin that circled the base of his throat drew her unwilling eyes.

'So?' Heath was speaking again, and she took a trembling breath. She could just see Greg in the room behind him, poring over some papers, and she clung to his presence, like an antidote to her own foolishness.

'I—I wanted to speak to you,' she said now, meeting Heath's critical gaze, and then felt unwelcome emotions stirring at the sudden frustration in his eyes.

'What about?' he demanded.

'It's—it's private.' She hated his impatience with her. 'Surely you can spare a moment. It might be a matter of life or death!'

'Is it?' Heath's eyes were more grey than green at that moment, and she wilted beneath his cool appraisal.

'No——'

'Then it can wait,' he declared, stepping back into the room, and before she could defend herself, he had closed the door upon her.

In her own room, Helen gave way to her own frustration and flung all the boxes and carriers she had previously laid reverently on the bed on to the floor. Heath was impossible, she thought bitterly. He deliberately went out of his way to humiliate her. She didn't want to think what Greg Marsden must have thought of the way Heath had spoken to her, and his rudeness was beyond bearing. What was he trying to do? Make her hate him? He had said it would be easy, and right now, she believed him.

She went down to dinner wearing the two-piece suit of jacket and drawstring pants. It was an attractive outfit, made of rose pink cotton, and it accentuated the darkness of her hair and the creamy tan she had already acquired.

All the time she was dressing for dinner, she had half expected Heath to come charging into her room, accusing her of goodness knows what misconduct, but he had not appeared, and she had eventually come to the conclusion that she had been over-sensitive. Perhaps Angela had taken the credit, after all. If Heath was paying her compliments, it was surely doubtful whether she would refuse them.

As on the previous evening, Heath's guests were gathered for dinner, this time in the leather-scented atmosphere of the library, where Greg was dispensing his host's hospitality. 'Hey there, young lady, what can I offer you this evening?' he demanded, when Helen appeared rather apprehensively in the doorway. 'Heath hasn't yet come down, but I'm sure he wouldn't object if I provided his favourite niece with an appetizer.'

'His *only* niece,' murmured Helen, rather doubtfully, glancing about her as she entered the room. Exchanging a smiling glance with Marion, her eyes moved on to Angela, draped with her usual grace in one of the armchairs. 'It's not like Heath to be late when he has guests.'

'He was late going up to change,' said Angela, speaking for the first time, snd Helen's nerves tightened at the decidedly smug expression on the other girl's face. 'Your uncle and I, we—er—we spent some time in the garden. After he'd finished his discussions with Mr Marsden.'

'Oh, hell, call me Greg, Angela,' exclaimed Marion's husband, handing Helen a dry sherry. 'Do you want a fill-up?' he enquired of his wife cheerfully. 'Might as well make the most of it, while Heath's not here.'

Helen sipped her sherry nervously, convinced that Angela's behaviour boded no good for herself. What had she and Heath talked about in the garden? Why was she sitting there looking like the cat who had just sampled the cream? Whatever conversation she and

Heath had had, had not ended on the embarrassed
note Helen had expected, and even though she told
herself she could not be blamed for Heath's mistake,
Helen still had the uneasy feeling she had not heard
the last of it.

Heath appeared as Mrs Gittens was announcing
dinner, apologising for his lateness. 'I got a call from
South America, just as I was about to come down,' he
offered in explanation, and Helen, darting a glance at
his dark face, could see no evidence of the anger she
had expected him to exhibit. On the contrary, his
eyes moved over her almost absently, and she
moistened her lips weakly as she followed Marion in
to dinner.

The meal was delicious: iced melon, with slices of
home-cured ham, chicken breasts cooked in wine and
cream, and to finish, a choice of sherry trifle,
raspberry mousse, or lemon meringue pie. Helen
actually enjoyed her food for once, and she was
content to take little part in the conversation that
accompanied it. Instead she allowed Marion and
Greg to direct the course of the discussion, and by
the end of the evening she was pleasantly relaxed
and sleepy from the amount of wine she had
consumed.

After coffee had been served in the drawing room,
Helen excused herself and went up to her room. Heath
and his guests would probably sit for ages yet, she
reflected, but she was tired. Although she had slept in
that morning, she had not slept awfully well the night
before, and she was glad that tonight at least she did
not have to worry about Heath. Evidently he and
Angela had had a pleasant conversation before dinner,
and she refused to consider Marion's comments as
anything more than idle gossip.

Taking off her earrings, she was examining her
complexion in the mirror when a knock came at her

door. Dropping the plain gold circles on to her dressing table, she went to answer it, stepping back aghast when she saw who it was. 'Heath!'

'Yes, Heath,' he agreed bleakly. 'Can I come in?'

Helen thought quickly. 'It's late. I—couldn't it wait until morning?'

'You haven't started to get undressed,' observed Heath, stepping past her into the room without waiting for an invitation. 'Shut the door, Helen, I want to talk to you, and I'd prefer it if our conversation was not overheard.'

Helen sighed, but after a few moments of silent hostility, she obediently closed the door. 'Very well,' she declared challengingly. 'What is it you want to say? You're being very mysterious. Won't your guests wonder where you are?'

'One of them, at least, knows where I am,' retorted Heath coldly. 'Angela, if you haven't guessed. But of course you must know why I'm here. You're not entirely without perception.'

'Thank you.' Helen's fingers betrayed her trepidation as she played with the cord that tied her pants. 'But you're wrong. I have no idea what you're so upset about.'

'Upset?' His mouth compressed angrily. 'Don't pretend with me, Helen. You know damn nicely what I'm—upset—about. You deliberately misled me, and I want an explanation.'

It took a great deal of courage to move away from the door, but Helen did it, passing him without looking at him to lift the brush from her dressing table. 'I didn't mislead you about anything, Heath,' she averred, starting to brush her hair. 'If you remember, I did try to talk to you this afternoon, but you were too busy.'

'The devil you did!' He snatched the brush out of

her hand. 'How was I supposed to know what you came to see me about?'

'You didn't give me the chance to tell you, did you?' retorted Helen hotly. 'As I recall it, you slammed the door in my face.'

'I was tied up at that moment——'

'That wasn't my fault.'

'You could have waited.'

'Where?' She stared up at him indignantly. 'Outside your study? What would you have had me do, lie down on the doormat, where you'd obviously like to keep me?'

'That's not true!' Heath's eyes darkened with anger. 'You should have told me last night that the clothes you were wearing were not new.'

'They were new to me,' declared Helen defensively.

'But Angela hadn't chosen them.'

'Angela said they were sloppy,' retorted Helen shortly. 'Why should I tell you that?'

He took a deep breath. 'Why did you do it?'

'Why did I do what?'

'Why did you refuse to wear the clothes Angela had chosen for you?'

She bent her head. 'They don't suit me.'

'What do you mean?'

'They're too old for me.'

'Too old?' Heath stared at her disbelievingly.

'Yes, they are.'

'Is that new?' He gestured to the suit she was wearing.

Helen hesitated. 'Yes——'

'So why didn't you wear it last night?'

She shrugged. 'I didn't have it last night. I—Marion and I bought this today.'

'I see.' Heath tapped the back of her hairbrush against his palm. 'And what does Marion think of these clothes Angela chose for you?'

'She agrees with me.'

'I suppose you told her some sob story about Angela not being sympathetic to your way of thinking; that you resent her because she's everything that you're not.'

'*No!*' Helen looked at him resentfully. 'That's a rotten thing to say.'

'But you did talk about her, didn't you?'

'Not much.'

'I'll bet!'

Heath was sceptical and Helen felt frustration rising inside her. 'You seem to think all I have to do is think about Angela Patterson,' she burst out angrily. 'Well, you're wrong. Just because you fawn on her every word, it doesn't mean I have to do the same. And while we're on the subject, you might as well know, she likes me just as much as I like her!'

'*Helen!*' Heath spoke ominously, but she ignored the warning.

'It's true,' she declared scornfully. 'And if you're planning on making her mistress of Matlock Edge, you're going to have to get rid of me first!'

'That might not be a bad idea,' he snarled, glaring at her furiously. 'You've been nothing but trouble since you came here!'

'*Oh!*' Helen caught her breath, the air expelled from her lungs in a painful gasp at his deliberate cruelty. 'How can you say that?'

'It's true!' he retorted, anger overriding all other emotions. 'You're a spoilt brat, and it's time you grew up.'

'Oh, is it?' Stung as she was, Helen could not allow him to get away with that. He had hurt her. He had hurt her badly, but she refused to go down without a fight. Maybe afterwards she would regret it, maybe afterwards she would despise herself for what she planned to do. But right now it was important to win the battle, if not the war, and casting all her inhibitions aside, she reached up and grasped his face between her two hands.

She caught him unawares, else otherwise she doubted she would have succeeded so far. His face was still contorted with fury after the harsh words they had exchanged, but his anger turned swiftly to disbelief when her soft lips touched his. With her mouth exploring the startled contours of his lips, he was too shocked to do anything but stand there, and Helen's fingers curled into the hair at the nape of his neck as she pressed herself close to his taut body.

'Helen,' he choked, his breath filling her mouth, but she would not let him go, and it was his hands that eventually forced her away from him, imprisoning her painfully at arm's length.

'You little bitch!' he swore unsteadily. 'You selfish little bitch!' and before she could prevent it, he sank down on to the bed behind him and jerked her on to his knee.

'You wouldn't, you wouldn't dare!' she gasped, as he groped for the hairbrush, but looking into his incensed dark face she knew he would. 'Heath, *don't*! *Please*!' she pleaded desperately, but she doubted he was even listening to her. His eyes had a curiously glazed appearance, as if his emotions were controlling his actions, and her heart palpitated wildly as he tore the cord of her pants loose and turned her on to her stomach.

Vital and youthful as she was, she was no match for his strength, and the hairbrush came down half a dozen times on her bare buttocks. It stung like mad, and it was all she could do to keep from crying out. It was only the fear that Angela might hear her that kept her quiet.

When he eventually let her go she was crying, silently, the tears running unheeded down her cheeks, dribbling into her mouth with salty persistence. She felt sick and more humiliated than she had ever felt before, and she stumbled to her feet clumsily, dragging the hated pants around her waist.

With her back to Heath, she didn't know what he was doing, but she prayed he would go. He had done everything he could to degrade her, she thought bitterly. Surely he would have the decency not to stay and take pleasure in his victory.

There were several minutes of complete silence, broken only by the uneven sound of Helen's breathing, and then Heath muttered: 'Oh, *God*!' and got abruptly to his feet. Helen froze, convinced he was going to continue his denigration of her character, but he didn't say another word. Instead, she heard him stride heavily across the floor, and seconds later her door slammed as he took his departure.

Only then did she realise how tight a hold she had kept on her emotions, and nausea flooded into her throat. She only reached the bathroom in time to empty her stomach into her basin, and tears mingled with the perspiration that dampened her quivering skin.

CHAPTER SEVEN

MRS GITTENS came into Helen's bedroom at eleven o'clock on Sunday morning to find the girl still slumped beneath the sprigged poplin sheet. She clicked her tongue reprovingly when her sharp eyes observed that Helen was not wearing a nightgown, and she gave an exclamation when she saw the clothes the girl had worn the night before strewn carelessly across the floor.

'Is this any way to treat a pretty outfit like this?' she demanded, catching sight of the covert glance Helen cast in her direction. 'I know you're not asleep, so you might as well answer me.'

Helen sniffed. 'You can take it away, Mrs Gittens. I never want to see it again.'

'What?' The housekeeper straightened. 'But it's a new suit, isn't it? Don't be silly, Helen. And why aren't you up? It's not like you to lie in bed till midday.'

'I'm not getting up.' Helen shrugged. 'And I mean it about the suit. Give it to your granddaughter, if you want to. I don't like it.'

Mrs Gittens ignored that. 'Come along,' she said briskly. 'You can't lie in bed all day.'

'Why not?' Helen avoided her eyes. 'Perhaps I'm not feeling well.'

'Aren't you? Do you want me to ask Mr Heathcliffe to call the doctor?'

'No.' Helen spoke hastily. 'I don't need a doctor. I just don't feel like getting up, that's all. Tell them I've got a cold.'

Mrs Gittens looked suspicious. 'And have you? Got a cold?'

Reader Service
FREEPOST
P.O. Box 236
Croydon
Surrey
CR9 9EL

YES! Please send me 2 FREE selected Masquerade romances together with my FREE oyster dishes and mystery gift and reserve a subscription for me. If I decide to subscribe I shall receive 4 new Masquerade titles every two months for £7.00, postage and packing FREE. If I decide not to subscribe I shall write to you within 10 days. The FREE books and gifts are mine to keep in any case. I understand that I can cancel or suspend my subscription at any time simply by writing to you. I am over 18 years of age.

10A9M

Name _____

Address _____

_____

_____ Postcode _____

Signature _____

Send no money now - take no risks

FREE GIFT

EXTRA BONUS GIFT

SURPRISE MYSTERY GIFT

'Not exactly.' Helen turned her head away.

'Then why are your eyes all puffy? Have you been crying?'

'Oh, for heaven's sake, must I suffer the third degree just because I don't feel like getting up?' exclaimed Helen unsteadily. 'I'm all right, honestly. Just leave me alone. I—I'll probably come down later. Maybe this afternoon—'

'Hmm.'

Mrs Gittens went away unwillingly, leaving the pants suit draped neatly over the basket chair by the window. Unable to lie there and look at it without thinking of what had happened, Helen slid out of bed, and bundled it into the bottom of her wardrobe, climbing back into bed again just as there was another knock at the door.

'Who is it?' she asked, muffling her voice under the sheet, and heard Marion's cheerful: 'Only me.' With an inward groan, she bade the other woman come in, and steeled her features carefully to meet another cross-examination.

'So there you are!' Marion looked bright and breezy as ever in a pair of green cotton slacks and a green and white spotted blouse. 'I was beginning to think you must have a hangover. I must say you do look a bit peaky this morning.'

Helen forced a smile. 'Just tired, that's all. I'm sorry if you think I'm being rude. Perhaps I've got a cold coming on.'

'Well, you do look a bit blotchy around the eyes,' agreed Marion, with her usual candour. 'I wondered whether you and Heath had had a row, actually. He's been like a bear with a sore head since you went to bed last night.'

Helen managed a shrug. 'Wh—where is he this morning?'

'He and Greg have gone to play golf. They left

about fifteen minutes ago. I don't really think Heath was in the mood for it, but you know what Greg's like. He can't wait to get out on the course.'

'Oh, I see.' Helen swallowed convulsively. 'Did—did they say when they'd be back?'

'I suppose around two-thirty,' remarked Marion carelessly. 'They're bound to finish at the nineteeth hole, and that's the time they close, isn't it?'

She nodded. 'Yes.'

Marion hesitated. 'You and Heath didn't have a row, did you? I mean—well, I feel responsible.'

'Responsible?' Helen was confused.

'Yes.' Marion sighed. 'Well, I persuaded you to buy all those clothes, didn't I? I should have kept my mouth shut and let Angela do her worst.'

'No, you shouldn't.' Helen couldn't let Marion think that. 'And Heath—Heath said nothing about the clothes we bought, honestly.' That at least was true.

'He didn't?' Marion looked suspicious.

'No.' Helen spoke firmly. 'As a matter of fact, I haven't even told him.'

'Oh, lord!' Marion looked dismayed. 'Then I've gone and put my foot in it again!'

Helen was tense. 'What do you mean?'

'Well——' Marion mused, 'when you didn't appear this morning, and Heath looked so bloody moody, I told him not to blame you for having spent all that money.'

'Oh, Marion!' Helen was appalled.

'I know—it was stupid.' Marion shook her head. 'But I thought you and he must have had words about it, and I wanted to explain why I'd done it. I told him what I thought of those dresses Angela Patterson had bought, and I explained that I didn't blame her exactly. That what she'd bought would probably suit her very well. But I tried to make him understand that what was suitable for a woman of Angela's age was not necessarily suitable for a teenager, and that Angela, not having had any children of her own, might not appreciate this.'

Helen closed her eyes briefly, and then opened them again. 'What did—Heath say?'

Marion lifted her shoulders. 'Not much. Oh, he was very polite, actually. He said he thought Angela had good dress sense, and that he would have expected her to make those kind of allowances. If she hadn't, then he would have a word with her, but for the present, he was prepared to reserve judgement.'

'Oh, Marion!' Helen felt miserable. 'He'll probably blame me for asking you to speak to him.'

'But you didn't.'

'Heath won't believe that.'

'Hey——' Marion looked at her closely, 'you and Heath have had a row, haven't you? Have you told me the truth?'

'Oh, yes. Yes.' Helen pressed her head back into the soft pillows. 'It was nothing to do with you. It was nothing to do with anyone. I'd really rather not talk about it, if you don't mind.'

'Of course.' Marion took her dismissal philosophically. 'Okay, love, I'll go. I've got to pack anyway. Greg and I are leaving about four. Will I see you before then?'

'Of course.' Helen endeavoured to pull herself together. 'If—if Heath and Greg have have gone out, I'll get up now. I just didn't feel like meeting Heath this morning.'

'I understand.' Marion moved towards the door. 'But if I dare to offer a bit of advice, I'd say you shouldn't take what Heath says too seriously. He cares about you—he cares about you a lot. That's why he sometimes says the wrong thing. Because he's trying so damn hard to do his best for you.'

Helen made a harsh disbelievingly sound. 'Are you sure?' she demanded bitterly. 'I increasingly get the feeling that I'm not wanted around here.'

'Oh, don't be silly!' Marion was impatient. 'Why, Heath's been like a father to you, you know he has.'

Helen bent her head. 'I don't need a father,' she muttered, and Marion's brows descended.

'What's that supposed to mean?'

'Oh—nothing.' Helen pushed her legs out of bed. 'I'll see you later.'

'Yes.' Marion surveyed her thoughtfully for a moment, then nodded her head. 'Yes, see you later,' she added briefly, and closed the door behind her.

A cool shower helped to bring Helen's sluggish limbs back to life, and by the time she had dried herself and cleaned her teeth, she was beginning to feel half decent. She refused to think about Heath, and what he might say when he got back. She refused even to contemplate the possible consequences of that scene in her bedroom. But she couldn't ignore the effects of the beating when she glimpsed the purplish bruising in the mirror, and felt the tenderness of her skin when she pulled on a pair of jeans.

It was a humid day, the hangover of the previous day's rain, but it was warm and Helen put on a camisole top she had bought the previous day. The simple garment left her neck and arms bare, and winding her hair about her hand she secured it on top of her head in a loose knot.

Downstairs, the first person she encountered was Mrs Gittens, and she raised her eyebrows sharply when she saw Helen. 'Feeling better?' she asked, without rancour, and the girl nodded. 'I guess Mrs Marsden told you Mr Heathcliffe has gone out,' she added drily. 'Miss Patterson is in the garden room reading the Sunday papers, if you want her.'

Helen didn't particularly want to see Angela, but

she felt obliged to acknowledge her existence, and she entered the glass-walled conservatory on reluctant feet. The other girl was seated comfortably on a chintz-covered sofa, her slim figure encased in flatteringly-fitted mauve pants and a crisp cotton blouse. As always, there was not a hair out of place, and Helen, in her black jeans and loose-fitting camisole, immediately felt as 'sloppy' as Angela had accused her of being.

'Oh, there you are,' the older girl said now, folding the newspaper she had been reading and tossing it on to the sofa beside her. 'I wondered how long it would take for you to find out that your uncle had left.'

Helen stiffened. 'I don't know what you mean.'

'Yes, you do.' Angela was complacent. 'Heath gave you a piece of his mind last night, didn't he? Don't bother to deny it. I can see from your expression that he did. And not before time, in my opinion. Letting him think I'd devised that ghastly outfit!'

Helen told herself she would not let Angela rile her, but it was difficult to remain indifferent when the other girl was trying so hard to annoy her. 'Heath approved of that—ghastly outfit, as you call it,' she declared evenly. 'He should. The shirt was his.'

Angela's lips thinned. 'He was being polite, that's all. Heath is always polite, or hadn't you noticed?'

Helen pushed her hands into the back pockets of her jeans. 'Since when do you call him Heath?' she demanded, and then wished she hadn't when Angela assumed a smug smile.

'Since last night,' she replied smoothly. 'He said as everyone else called him Heath, why shouldn't I?' She paused, her eyes surveying Helen in a way she didn't like, and then continued: 'By the way, I wouldn't wear a top like that without a bra, if I were you. Those cords at the front are rather—revealing, and to be honest, your breasts are too big to do without any support.' She glanced down at her own slim figure

with some satisfaction before adding? 'I don't need a
bra. My breasts are small and high. Yours ...' She
shook her head. 'Just a suggestion, of course.'

Helen's face blazed with colour now, and she knew
an almost irresistible urge to scratch Angela's eyes out,
but she controlled it. Turning away, she cast a
surreptitious glance at the low neckline of the camisole,
but she couldn't see anything to object to. Her breasts
were full, it was true, but they were not pendulous as
Angela had implied, and her wrist brushed against them
reassuringly, as if to convince herself that they were still
as firm as when she got dressed. Angela was just being
bitchy, that's all, she told herself indignantly, but she
couldn't help wishing she was as slim as her adversary.

As Marion had predicted, Heath and Greg arrived
back soon after half-past two. The three women had
eaten their lunch earlier, but Mrs Gittens had left a
cold buffet laid in the dining room for the men.
Marion joined them while they ate, and Helen could
hear the sound of their conversation, if not the actual
words. Curled up in a chair in the library, she half
hoped she could get away without being seen until
dinner, but the Marsdens' departure necessitated her
appearance.

'Be good, love,' Marion told her affectionately,
giving Helen a warm kiss. 'Don't forget, if you get fed
up with life at Matlock, you can always come and stay
with us in London.'

'Thanks, Marion.' Aware of Heath's eyes upon
them, Helen returned her embrace and then backed
off a little nervously as Greg came to say farewell.

'Just don't grow up too quickly,' he declared, respect-
ing her reticence and confining himself to a kiss on her
cheek. 'What would he do if you weren't around?' he
demanded, flicking his thumb in Heath's direction.

It was only a rhetorical question, but it was not one
Helen wanted to consider just then. Avoiding Heath's

eyes, she stepped out on to the gravel courtyard to wave goodbye, and as she did so, she wished rather foolishly that she was going with them, if only to get away from Heath until she had had time to think.

To her relief, Heath seemed as eager as she was to avoid a confrontation after the Marsdens had departed. Leaving the two girls to their own devices, he disappeared into his study, and deciding she was not obliged to entertain Angela today, Helen escaped to her own room.

Switching on the stereo unit Heath had had installed for her personal enjoyment, she flicked carelessly through her records, choosing one of the new wave of groups, whose music was more in keeping with her mood. She still felt raw and vulnerable, and it had hurt to realise Heath had no intention of apologising. No doubt, so far as he was concerned, it had been just another of their flare-ups, but for Helen it had been much more than that. Once and for all, he had exhibited his dislike of any emotional demonstration on her behalf, and the nebulous dreams she had had concerning their relationship had been proved to be just so much hot air. He didn't see her as a woman, certainly not as a woman he could become attracted to, and she was wasting her time imagining that he would ever change.

Locked into her mood of remorse, Helen prepared for dinner that evening with an air of indifference. Ignoring the pretty things she and Marion had bought on Saturday, she chose instead one of the dresses Angela had chosen, allowing its clinging lines to emphasise the rounded curves of her figure.

Heath and Angela were in the library when she went downstairs, and she hesitated a moment before interrupting their conversation. But then, steeling herself to face whatever comment Heath might care to make, she stepped determinedly into the room, and had the satisfaction of witnessing his surprise.

'Can I get you a drink?' he asked, after a moment, and she nodded.

'A sherry, thank you,' she acknowledged, and ignoring Angela's speculative glance, she seated herself on the leather sofa below the windows.

Observing the dress Angela was wearing, Helen couldn't help but compare her spare slenderness with her own appearance. As Marion had assured her, the dark blue sheath would have suited Angela so much better, and she hoped rather grimly that Heath liked what he had created.

'Have you known the Marsdens long?' enquired Angela, during dinner. The bulk of the conversation had been left to her—Heath seemingly absorbed in his own thoughts and Helen broodingly morose—and her host took some time before making his response.

'About twenty years, I guess,' he said at last, as if he had expected Helen to answer her. 'We used to go to the same school. When my father died, he came to work for me.'

'In computers?' Angela tried to sustain his interest, and Heath frowned.

'Not initially, no. Greg's good with figures, and he became my financial adviser.'

'Oh, I see.' Angela paused. 'His wife seems older than he is.'

Helen's head jerked up then, but realising it was a deliberate ploy to bring her into the conversation, she quickly lowered it again. It was again left to Heath to reply, and he lifted his shoulders carelessly as he gave his opinion.

'I don't think so,' he declared slowly. 'I was best man at their wedding, and as I recall it, Marion's about the same age.'

Angela crumbled her roll delicately. 'I suppose it's difficult for me to judge. She's so much older.'

Helen took long steady breaths. She would not be brought into this, she told herself fiercely, but Angela's ingenious comments were designed to frustrate her.

'They're a nice couple,' said Heath at last, either unaware of Angela's bitchiness or dismissing it. 'Marion thinks a lot of Helen. She has a son and a daughter almost the same age.'

'Really?'

Helen thought Angela made it sound as if she had imagined Marion's children would be years older. But just then she was more concerned with the inflection in Heath's voice, and she chanced a look at him to see if she could read anything from his expression. But his face was averted his eyes studying the wine in his glass, and without their revealing message she could make no confident assessment.

'I have to go away tomorrow,' he said suddenly, startling both women by the unexpectedness of his announcement.

'Away?' All of a sudden Helen was unable to remain silent. 'Away where? London?'

'No. Montevideo,' replied Heath flatly, meeting her gaze now without revealing any of his thoughts, and she gulped.

'Montevideo!' echoed Angela, almost as hastily. 'But that's in South America!'

Helen paused only long enough to give Angela an irritated glance before exclaiming accusingly: 'You've not mentioned this before.'

'I didn't know before,' retorted Heath, with annoying coolness. 'You may remember, I got a phone call from South America last evening.'

'And you knew then!'

'No.' He spoke distantly. 'I received another call this evening. I'll be away about a week. I'm sure you'll be well looked after in my absence.'

Helen looked down at her plate. It was over a year since Heath had last visited South America, and not long ago he had commented that he was unlikely to be called upon to undertake such a journey again. He had men who worked for him, managers and directors, who could be relied upon to act in his best interests, men to whom a trip to South America provided a welcome break in their busy lives. Yet now Heath was proposing to make this trip himself, and Helen couldn't help thinking that she was to blame for his sudden decision. Like her, he wanted to get away; like her, he felt he needed time to think. What worried her most was the possibility that he might decide he had had enough, and in spite of her humiliation, Helen knew she would rather live with Heath as his niece than not live with him at all.

The telephone rang again as they were having coffee in the sitting room, but this time the call was for Angela. Left alone with Heath, Helen knew she had to take this chance to try and heal the breach between them, but her tentative opening was overridden by his more-powerful voice.

'I suppose I should apologise,' he said stiffly, startling her into silence. 'If that dress is an example of Angela's choice of clothes for you, then you were right to refuse to wear them.' He sighed. 'Once again, I've overreached my responsibilities. I have to remember you're too old to be treated like a little girl.'

Helen didn't know what to say, and Heath impaled her with an ice-green gaze. 'That's not to say the spanking wasn't justified. It was,' he stated harshly. 'But I am not usually so barbaric, and for that, I do offer my apologies.'

Helen moistened her lips. 'Is that why you're going away?' she asked impulsively, and saw the look of loathing that crossed his face.

'Why should you imagine that?' he demanded

tautly. 'I'm going to Montevideo on business. What possible connection can that have to what happened last night?'

Helen shrugged. 'It seems rather sudden, that's all.'

He arched his brows. 'It happens that way sometimes.'

'Does it?' She looked at him through her lashes. 'You told me a few weeks ago that you wouldn't have to go there again. You said you could delegate all your——'

'This is different,' Heath interrupted her shortly. Then he sighed. 'If you must know, Señor Garcia has insisted that I sign the contract between us myself. And as it happens, his eldest daughter is getting married next week also. He's invited me to the wedding, and this way, I can accomplish both feats. All right?'

Helen pursed her lips. 'Señor Garcia has—other daughters?'

'Three, I think,' agreed Heath, getting up to pour himself a glass of brandy. 'Now, are you satisfied? I'm obliged to go.'

'Take me with you!'

The words slipped out almost involuntarily, but they could not be withdrawn, and Heath turned to face her, his face dark and forbidding. 'No.'

'Why not?'

He took a mouthful of the brandy, and then said harshly: 'You're not invited.'

'I don't believe you. Señor Garcia knows about me. He used to send me little gifts from time to time, didn't he? That painted fan, and the doll, dressed in——'

'You're not going,' said Heath flatly. 'Whether or not you were invited is irrelevant. You stay here, with Angela.'

Helen's chin quivered. 'You—you bastard——' she

choked, then broke off abruptly as Heath took a menacing step towards her.

'What did you say?' he demanded, but before he could reach her, Angela reappeared.

'So sorry for the interruption,' she said, sitting down on the couch again and picking up her coffee cup. 'It was a friend of my father's. He just wanted to reassure himself that I was happy here.' She paused, and then added demurely: 'Of course, I told him I was .'

Helen was in that drowsy state between sleeping and waking when Heath came to her room. She had dozed only fitfully throughout the night, so that when he opened her bedroom door she was immediately alert to his presence. It was light outside, so she guessed it must be morning, but the coolness of the air suggested it was not long after sun-up.

'Oh—you're awake,' he said shortly, as she struggled up on to her pillows. 'I just came to say goodbye. I'm leaving in a few minutes.'

'So soon?' Helen was too bemused to sustain any hostility, and Heath's expression softened at her unguarded exclamation.

'It's seven-thirty,' he told her, the darkness of his suit contrasting sharply with the silvery lightness of his hair. 'My flight leaves Heathrow at a quarter to twelve. Ormerod is driving me to Manchester to catch the shuttle.'

Helen sighed. 'How long will you be gone?'

'You know—about a week.'

She looked anxious. 'I'll miss you.'

'I'll miss you, too,' agreed Heath tautly. 'But I guess this trip will give us both a break. And give you and Angela a better chance to get used to one another.'

She bent her head. 'If you say so.'

'Oh, Helen——' with an exclamation of frustration,

Heath came down on the bed beside her, uncaring that the sheet might muss his dark pants. 'What do you want me to say?' he demanded, taking one of her hands between both of his. 'Last night—well, the least said about last night the better, don't you agree? I don't like being called a bastard, not by anyone. And don't pretend you didn't use the word. My hearing's still as acute as it ever was.'

Helen moved her shoulders helplessly, taking care to keep the sheet tucked under her arms. 'You just seem to do things to hurt me,' she murmured unwillingly, and his fingers tightened round hers as he expelled his breath impatiently.

'To hurt you!' he exclaimed. 'I don't do things to hurt you,' he protested. 'For heaven's sake, Helen, I care about you too much for that.'

'You do?' she ventured to look at him and he gave a deep sigh. With her hair loose and tumbled about her shoulders and the delicate blush of colour in her cheeks, she had a natural sensuality, and Heath was not unaware of it.

'Of course I do,' he told her roughly. 'All right, so I lost my temper on Saturday night, but surely that was understandable. You must learn not to take advantage of our relationship.'

Helen hunched her shoulders. 'You used not to object. You used to like me to kiss you.'

'That was different.' He released her hand abruptly. 'And you know it, Helen. You're growing up now, and—and what you did—well, with anyone else it could have got you into a lot of trouble.'

'But not with you,' she tendered softly, and sensed the sudden tensing of his body.

'No, not with me,' he agreed shortly. 'And stop looking at me like that! I don't want us to part in anger.'

She looked away from him. 'All right, go then,' she

said, pushing back her hair with annoyingly unsteady fingers. 'Have a good trip. Give Señor Garcia my regards.'

'Helen!' His use of her name was tormented, and relenting a little she looked back at him.

'Goodbye,' she whispered, her eyes filled with unshed tears, and with a groan of anguish, Heath bent towards her.

– 'Goodbye,' he said, but he said it against her mouth, and her lips parted in instinctive response. With a little moan deep in her throat, she wound her arms around his neck and kissed him back, and the sweetness of her lips was an irresistible invitation.

'Ah, Helen——' he muttered, his hands curving unwillingly over her shoulders, and she lifted herself from the pillows to facilitate his embrace. With unknowing sexuality, she invited his response, and the urgent passion of his kiss became a moist and searching intimacy.

The protective sheet was forgotten and it fell away to expose the thrusting beauty of her breasts, and it was only when she parted the buttons of his shirt and he felt the taut peaks probing at the hair-roughened skin of his chest that he seemed to come to his senses. But when he pressed her away from him, she made no attempt to cover herself. Instead she faced him proudly, uncaring that he might despise her, and his fingers dug painfully into her shoulders as he met that deliberate challenge.

'No, Helen,' he said, but his voice was as unsteady as hers had been earlier, and she knew he was not as indifferent as he maintained.

'Why not?' she breathed, tipping her head so that she could rub her cheek against the back of his hand, and with a muffled groan he got swiftly to his feet.

'What am I going to do with you, Helen?' he demanded harshly. 'For God's sake, what do you think I am?'

'I think you're a man and I'm a woman,' replied Helen softly. 'I think you want me, and I know I want you.'

He swore savagely. 'Want? *Want?* What do you know about wanting? How many men have you *wanted?*'

'Only you,' she replied honestly, and he swore again.

'You're crazy,' he declared. 'You know nothing about the relationship between a man and a woman!'

'I know what happens.'

'From biology textbooks, no doubt,' retorted Heath grimly. 'For God's sake, Helen, you know nothing about what it's like to have a man make love to you. You talk blandly about sex, as if you were an experienced woman of the world! You're not. You're a teenager; a crazy teenager, who doesn't know the first thing about it.'

'You do,' said Helen innocently, and Heath scowled.

'Don't talk like that.'

'Is it important to you?' she asked suddenly. 'Would you prefer it if I were experienced?'

'For God's sake, *no!*' Heath raked savage fingers across his scalp. 'And that doesn't mean I want you as you are! Helen, listen to me—listen to me carefully: you're my responsibility, but that's all there is between us.'

'I don't believe you!' She spoke indignantly, but there was a glimmer of doubt in her voice, and he pressed home his advantage.

'I mean it,' he said tensely. 'We've known each other too long. We're too—closely related. I don't think of you in that way.'

She groped blindly for the sheet, dragging it over her. 'When—when you kissed me——' she began, but Heath interrupted her.

'I felt sorry for you,' he declared bleakly. 'I'd been rough with you, and I was sorry. It shouldn't have happened. It wouldn't have happened if I hadn't felt so bloody guilty.'

Helen looked at him bitterly. 'So why are you hanging about?' she exclaimed. 'Why don't you go to Manchester or Montevideo, or wherever it is you're going? You've had your little victory. Now leave me alone.'

'God, Helen——'

'Please go away,' she cried, rolling over to bury her face in the pillow, and with a muttered oath Heath walked out, slamming the door behind him.

CHAPTER EIGHT

OF course, as soon as she heard the Mercedes pull away, Helen regretted sending him off like that. For the remainder of the day she plagued herself with thoughts of how she would feel if his plane came down or some other disaster befell him. But by the next morning she was able to breathe more easily. No plane crashes had been reported during the night, and so far as she could ascertain, Heath had reached his destination safely.

Nevertheless, she missed him desperately. The house wasn't the same with the knowledge that he would not be coming home in the evenings. Even Angela's jibes had no power to penetrate the wall of reserve she built round herself, and the days passed slowly, dictated by the weather.

On fine, sunny days the two girls spent most of their time outdoors, swimming in the pool, or sunbathing on the patio. Safe behind the pages of a book, Helen was not obliged to be sociable, and as Angela basked in the sunshine like a seal, she made few demands upon Helen.

But by Thursday the weather had changed, and imprisoned indoors, Angela seemed to take a delight in keeping Helen under her eye every minute. She wanted to know where Helen was going, even when she went to the bathroom, and the younger girl grew pale and listless, desperate for some diversion.

On Friday morning Helen determined that today things were going to be different. Instead of staying in bed until Mrs Gittens came to disturb her, she got up

at seven o'clock, and pulling on a leather jerkin over
her tee-shirt and jeans, she made her way down the
back stairs and out through the kitchen garden.

It was a relief to wheel the Honda out of its shed,
and donning her helmet, she swung her leg across the
saddle. With a bit of luck, she'd make her escape
before Miles came to work. He, like Angela, was
someone else she had no wish to encounter this
morning.

Realising Miles would use the private road to reach
the house, Helen took off over the fields, the little
machine bucking bravely as it negotiated the muddy
bogs left by the rain. Her legs were getting splashed
with mud, too, but she didn't care, and for the first
time since Heath went away, she felt a lifting of her
spirits.

Beyond Jacob's Hollow, she came out on to the
Starforth road, and stopped a moment to examine the
damage. As far as she could see, she had only covered
herself and the motorbike with a coating of soft earth,
and once it had dried it would easily brush away. Her
jeans might have to be washed, of course, but that
wasn't important. They had already been washed half
a dozen times, and they were unlikely to shrink any
more.

The road was busy with early morning traffic, and
after travelling for some miles with a continual escort,
she turned off on to a country lane, just before the
village, bouncing along more happily without the
noisy roar of other vehicles.

She came to another village called Shipwell, and
paused on the green to read the signpost. Evidently
she could take the road to Bishopston from here,
which was some miles further on than Matlock Edge
in the opposite direction, which would mean she had
completed a circuit of the estate, without riding over
any more of Heath's land.

She was perhaps halfway to Bishopston when the motorbike began to sputter and finally died on her. No matter how she tried, it refused to start again, and she looked about her helplessly, aware of how vulnerable she was. It was ages since she'd seen a signpost, ages since she'd seen any kind of habitation other than a farmworker's cottage, and who could possibly help her when she didn't know what was wrong?

Sighing, she tried to think positively. She was, she estimated, approximately eight miles from Bishopston and probably an equal number from Shipwell. There didn't seem much point in going back. She would be nearer home at Bishopston. Perhaps if she could push the Honda to a garage there they might be able to do something for her, and if not, at least she would be able to phone home and let Mrs Gittens know she was all right. The old housekeeper would worry terribly if she found Helen was missing, and for the first time she realised how selfish she had been in riding off without even leaving a note.

It was amazing how heavy the Honda was, now that she had to push it. It made her wish she had stayed on the main road after all. She would certainly have felt less isolated, and seen more garages, too, than on a winding country lane that merely connected two villages.

She had been walking for almost half an hour and her legs and arms were aching and she was soaked with sweat, when she heard the sound of a vehicle. Although it was not a sunny morning, it was warm, and the leather jacket which had seemed ideal for riding had begun to stick to her neck and arms. She turned her head wearily when she heard the engine, and then pulled the motorbike off the road when a Land Rover came into sight.

The Land Rover slowed however as it neared her, and Helen prepared herself to parry the comments of some would-be knight-errant. With Heath's warning still ringing in her ears, she was in no mood to accept a lift from anyone she didn't know, and she gripped the handlebars tightly as the vehicle stopped beside her.

'Want some assistance?'

The voice did not have the broad West Yorkshire accent she had expected, and Helen looked up unwillingly to find a man in his early twenties looking down at her sympathetically.

'Oh—no,' she declined firmly, accompanying her refusal with a faint smile nevertheless. 'I can manage, thank you.'

'Have you run out of petrol!' asked the young man casually, pushing open his door and getting out. 'I know these machines do a fantastic number of miles to the gallon, but they do need refilling sometimes.'

'I don't know. I never thought.' Cursing herself, Helen bent over the fuel tank and removed the cap. Peering inside, she saw to her disgust that it did indeed appear to be empty, and she sighed. Damn it, why hadn't Miles refilled the tank? He had always done so in the past.

'It is empty, I see,' the young man commented, making his own inspection before looking up at her quizzically. 'I guess you're going to have to push it some distance. There's not another garage until you reach Bishopston.'

Helen pursed her lips. 'Thanks for the information,' she muttered.

'My pleasure.' The young man swung open his door. 'Of course, I could always dump the bike in the back of the Rover and drive you there, if you'd let me. But if, as you say, you can manage without my assistance, there's nothing more I can suggest.'

Helen pressed her lips together, looking down at the Honda with some frustration. She couldn't really blame Miles for not filling the petrol tank. She should have checked it herself before she left. Heath had always advised her to check the tank at regular intervals, and if she hadn't been so all-fired keen to get away this morning, she would have done so.

'Well?'

The man was waiting for her reply, and she looked up at him uncertainly. He looked harmless enough, she thought doubtfully. He looked rather nice, actually. Brown-haired, brown-skinned, with warm brown eyes to match; he didn't look like a villain, but how was she to judge?

'I promise I'm not planning to abduct you,' he remarked suddenly, as if reading her thoughts and Helen flushed.

'Am I so transparent?'

'Well, you've evidently been told not to accept lifts from strange men,' he agreed drily. 'And I'd endorse that. But I'm not entirely strange. Your uncle's land and my father's has a mutual boundary.'

'My uncle's land——' Helen broke off. 'You know who I am?'

He grinned. 'At a guess, I'd say you were Helen Mortimer, am I right?'

Helen gasped. 'Yes. But——' She paused. 'Who are you?'

'Nigel Fox,' he replied, at once, and Helen's eyes widened.

'You're—Sir Malcolm Fox's son?'

'The same.' He gave a rueful grimace. 'So—will you accept my offer? Or do you still have doubts?'

Helen hesitated. She had only his word that he was Nigel Fox, and in any case, his identity meant nothing to her. Heath knew the Foxes, of course. They belonged to the same golf club, they supported the same charities, and they had mutual business interests. But Heath had never spoken of the son, or encouraged her to get to know him.

'Would you like to see my driver's licence?'

Nigel Fox was regarding her with slightly amused eyes now, and Helen quickly came to a decision. He was not so big that she need have any worries of him overpowering her, and in any case, he'd be driving the vehicle, which would occupy his hands.

'I'd like a lift,' she said determinedly. 'Thank you.'

'Okay.' Nigel grinned. 'You get in while I put your motorbike into the back. Thank God it's not a bigger machine—these things weigh a ton!'

Helen giggled as he hefted the Honda into the back of the Land Rover, and then came round to join her in front, wiping his hands on an oily rag. In a grey-checked shirt and tweed jacket, shabby riding breeches covering his thighs, he didn't look much like a baronet's son, but his smile was infectious as he slid behind the wheel.

'Okay,' he said. 'Where do you want to go? To Carron, to the garage in Bishopston, or home?'

Helen moistened her lips. 'Carron? That's your home, isn't it?'

'That's right,' Nigel nodded. 'I thought you might like to come and have some breakfast before you continued on your way.'

'That's very kind of you, but——'

'—you'd rather go home.'

'Well, I'd rather go to the garage in Bishopston,' confesed Helen ruefully. 'If you take me home, there's bound to be a post-mortem.'

'Won't there be one anyway?' asked Nigel, starting the engine. 'I mean, it's nearly nine o'clock, and I'd guess you left home before your uncle was up.'

'Oh, Heath's away,' exclaimed Helen carelessly. 'He's in South America. There's only Mrs Gittens, that's our housekeeper, and Angela of course.'

'Angela?'

'Angela Patterson,' replied Helen flatly. 'She's—

staying with us at the moment. She's a—friend of Heath's.'

'Heath?' Nigel frowned. 'Is that what you call your uncle?'

'He's not my——' began Helen quickly, and then changed her mind. 'Rupert Heathcliffe,' she agreed, looking out of the window. 'Is this all your land? Do you farm it yourselves?'

'Some,' said Nigel, nodding. 'I was sent to agricultural college to learn all about modern farming methods, but a lot of the land has had to be sold to meet taxes. We still have one or two tenant farmers, people who've worked for my family since the year dot, but compared to the estate as it was in my grandfather's day, it's much depleted.'

Helen inclined her head. 'I suppose you're sorry.'

'Not really.' Nigel shrugged. 'What do we need all this land for? I'd prefer to have fewer responsibilities, and more time to do the things I wanted to do.'

'Such as?' Helen was interested.

'Oh—I guess I just like my freedom,' he responded easily. 'How about you? What do you do?'

She bent her head. 'Not a lot. If Heath—if my uncle had his way I'd still be in school.'

'In school?' He stared at her disbelievingly. 'How old are you?'

'Nearly eighteen.' Helen was defensive. 'Heath believes in education. The trouble was, I didn't know what I was being educated for. I've never had a job.'

He shook his head. 'There's no likely boy-friend on the horizon?' he queried, and she gave him a sidelong look.

'No.' She paused. 'Are you married?'

'Who would have me?' Nigel grimaced.

'You are, as a friend of mine would say, fishing for compliments,' declared Helen, relaxing. 'I'm sure you know exactly how eligible your father's title makes you.'

'Is that all?' He gave her a wounded look, and she laughed.

'You know what I mean. Most girls would like to be called Lady something-or-other?'

'Would you?'

'Me?' Helen gurgled. 'Oh, no, not me. I just can't see myself as *Lady* anything, can you?'

'I think you'd carry it off beautifully,' he declared gallantly. 'Well, here we are at Bishopston. Are you sure you wouldn't like me to take you all the way?'

'Oh, no.' Helen looked about her eagerly, and was relieved to see a garage just across the road. 'This is fine. I'm very grateful, Mr Fox, honestly.'

'Nigel.'

'Nigel, then.' She pressed his arm impulsively before climbing out. 'I hope I haven't messed up your Land Rover. I'm very muddy.'

'That's what Land Rovers are for,' said Nigel, hoisting the motorcycle out on to the road again. 'Here, I'll wheel it across to the garage for you.'

The petrol pump attendant knew Nigel and attended to them straight away. 'Put it on our account, Ted,' he said, causing Helen to protest loudly, but he insisted, and she gave in.

'You really have been a good Samaritan,' she exclaimed, pulling on her helmet again before mounting. 'I don't know how to thank you.'

'Let me take you out to dinner tomorrow evening,' declared Nigel simply. 'I could pick you up at your place about seven-thirty. I'd book a table at the Bell in Starforth.'

'Oh, I don't know . . .' Helen was doubtful, chewing on her lower lip anxiously as she considered his invitation.

'You can introduce me to your uncle, and I'll assure him of my best intentions,' Nigel added whimsically, and she expelled her breath uncertainly as she gave the matter her full attention.

'Heath will still be away,' she murmured, swinging her leg across the motorbike. 'I don't know what he would say.'

'It's not your uncle I'm inviting,' Nigel reminded her softly. 'You're not a child, Helen. Surely you can make your own decisions? Either you want to come out with me or you don't—it's as uncomplicated as that.'

She sighed. 'All right,' she said, after another moment's thought. 'Why not?' Heath was always encouraging her to go out with young people of her own age, and Nigel Fox was not more than twenty-three or four.

'Great!' Nigel looked pleased. 'Seven-thirty it is, then. I'll see you tomorrow.'

'Tomorrow,' agreed Helen, feeling a fluttering of excitement inside her. It was the first time she had made a date without Heath's permission, and she liked the feeling of independence it gave her.

It was nearly ten o'clock when she got back to Matlock, and as she had half expected, it was Mrs Gittens who was most concerned about her disappearance. 'Wherever have you been?' she exclaimed, as Helen sauntered into the house after leaving the motorcycle propped up by the front door. 'As soon as young Miles confirmed that the Honda had gone, I started to worry, and I do think you could have phoned if you'd known you were going to be this late.'

'I ran out of petrol,' exclaimed Helen, when she could get a word in. 'The bike just gave out on me. I had to walk miles to the nearest garage. And there wasn't a phone in sight.'

'Oh, my God!' Mrs Gittens stared at her aghast. 'Dear heaven, Helen, anything could have happened to you! Where were you when you ran out of petrol? How far did you have to push that heavy machine?'

'About four miles——'

'Four miles!' Mrs Gittens gasped.

'It would have been farther,' added Helen reluctantly, 'but I got a lift.'

'A lift? A lift who with? Helen, don't tell me you let some man pick you up!' Mrs Gittens pressed a hand to her cheek.

'He did pick me up, yes, but—wait!' this as the housekeeper would have intervened again, 'he wasn't a complete stranger. It was Nigel Fox.'

'Nigel Fox?' Mrs Gittens looked blank. 'Nigel Fox? Who's that?'

'Sir Malcolm Fox's son,' explained Helen firmly. 'You know the Foxes—from Carron Hall?'

'Those Foxes.' Mrs Gittens looked doubtful. 'Are you sure?'

'Of course I'm sure.' Helen gave an exclamation of impatience. 'In any case, you can meet him yourself, if you want to. He's taking me out to dinner tomorrow night. He's calling for me at half past seven.'

Mrs Gittens clasped her hands together. 'You're going out with him?'

'Haven't I just said so?'

'But what do you know about him?'

Helen groaned. 'What do I need to know? He's nice. You'll like him. He's young and good-looking, and he's fun to be with.' She paused, and then when the housekeeper still looked unconvinced, she added: 'You know Heath's always saying I should have friends of my own age. Well, Nigel is my age—or near enough.'

Mrs Gittens shook her head. 'I don't know what Mr Heathcliffe will say,' she insisted.

'What can he say? He's not here,' exclaimed Helen shortly. 'For goodness' sake, Mrs Gittens, we're only going to the Bell in Starforth. He's not selling me to some white-slaver!'

Angela reacted quite differently when she heard the news, and the younger girl reflected rather uncharitably that that was probably because she found Helen's presence inhibiting. If this friendship with Nigel Fox developed in the way Angela evidently hoped, it would leave the field clear for her to advance her relationship with Heath.

However, in spite of Helen's determination to be her own mistress and accept this invitation, she found herself in something of a quandary when she went to bed that night. All day she had maintained, to herself and to others, that she wanted to go out with Nigel Fox, but in the unwelcome isolation of her bedroom, she acknowledged that her desire was half-hearted, at best. It wasn't that she didn't like Nigel. She did. He seemed a very presentable young man. It was just that for so long she had avoided this kind of a situation in case Heath got the wrong idea, and even though he had told her he had no use for her affection, she couldn't turn it off just like that. It was all too easy to remember how Heath had made her feel when he kissed her. None of the boys she had known and been friendly with had ever aroused the feelings in her that Heath did, and she didn't want him to think she had changed her mind. If she started going out with Nigel Fox on a regular basis, Heath might imagine she had stopped loving him, and for all her inexperience, she knew that was unlikely to happen.

Yet wasn't this just what Heath himself wanted? He had told her, brutally enough, that he had didn't care about her in that way, that he regarded her as his niece, and nothing more. Wasn't she wasting her life by imagining he might change his mind, when no amount of pleading had softened his heart? She was his responsibility, that was what he had said, and the unspoken implication was that she was a responsibility he could do without.

In spite of her misgivings, Helen did enjoy Nigel's

company. He called for her, as planned, and met both
Angela and Mrs Gittens before they took their
departure.

'Your Miss Patterson is quite a stunner, isn't she?'
he commented as his elderly M.G. accelerated down
the drive. 'A bit cool for my taste,' he added,
grimacing at Helen, 'but probably appealing to
someone who likes their wine chilled. I don't.'

She smiled. 'You don't have to say that. I don't
mind.'

'I mean it.' He was very definite. 'You—you're like
a fine burgundy, rich and dark and full-blooded.' He
gave her a warm glance. 'There's nothing chilling
about you, Helen, believe me!'

It was good to know that Nigel at least did not find
Angela more appealing. On the contrary, he did his
best throughout the evening to make her feel she was
the most attractive girl he had ever met, and Helen
flowered visibly. Freed from the restraints placed
upon her by Heath's presence, she allowed her own
personality to flourish, and several pairs of male eyes
sought their table every time her infectious laughter
rang out.

'I like your dress,' Nigel said on one occasion, his
eyes moving caressingly over her bare shoulders, and
she looked down pleasurably at the creamy chiffon. It
was one of the items Marion had chosen, and its off-
the-shoulder style and dipped waistline were very
becoming, accentuating her dark colouring and the
golden texture of her tan. Without Marion's intervention, she would have to have worn one of the
dresses Angela had chosen, and she knew the other
girl's eyes had narrowed when she appeared dressed as
she was.

They finished dinner about half past nine, and
walked for a while in the garden of the hotel. It was
pleasant meandering along the shrub-lined paths that

led down to the river, and Helen was quite regretful when it was time for her to leave.

'I have enjoyed myself,' she told Nigel, when he delivered her back to Matlock. 'Thank you for taking me. I haven't had so much fun for ages.'

'Then we must do it again,' he declared, his arm along the back of her seat, his fingers playing lightly with the frilly neckline of her dress. 'How about next Tuesday? Do you fancy seeing a film in Bradford? We could have a Chinese supper afterwards, if you like.'

'Oh . . .' Helen moistened her dry lips, 'I'm not sure about that.'

'Why not?' His expression was shadowed in the muted light from the dash. 'You've just said we've had fun together. Why shouldn't we have fun again?'

Helen hesitated. 'Heath will be back by then,' she volunteered awkwardly. 'I'd have to ask him.'

'Okay, so ask him.' Nigel was impatient. 'I don't see how he can object. I'm only inviting you to the movies.'

Helen nodded. 'All right,' she said after a moment, 'I'll see what I can do. Can I ring you later? When I know for sure.'

'I'll ring you,' said Nigel firmly. 'That way I'll be sure you don't forget.' He paused. 'Goodnight, Helen. You really are terribly sweet.'

His lips brushed hers lightly and then settled there, and the arm which had been along the back of her seat closed about her, bringing her closer. His lips were firm and warm, not at all like Miles' but not like Heath's either, and although she tried to relax with him, eventually she had to pull away.

'I'd better go in,' she said, rather breathlessly, fumbling for the catch of the door, and Nigel leant across to assist her.

'Until Tuesday,' he said, his lips touching her

cheek, and Helen nodded her head quickly before scrambling out on to the drive.

She encountered Mrs Gittens in the hall, and the housekeeper looked her over with a mixture of disapproval and relief. 'So he brought you back safely,' she remarked, hiding her affection for the girl beneath a brusque inconsequence. 'It's just as well for him. Your uncle was disappointed to learn that you were out.'

'My uncle—*Heath*!' Helen gazed at Mrs Gittens disbelievingly. 'Is Heath back?' Her eyes darted anxiously towards the stairs. 'I didn't know he was coming home today.'

'He wasn't and he hasn't,' declared Mrs Gittens flatly. 'He rang.' She glanced at the tall grandfather clock that stood at the foot of the stairs. 'About two hours ago.'

'Oh, *no*!' Helen's spirits drooped abruptly.

'Oh, yes. He wanted to speak to you, but as you were out, he spoke to Miss Patterson instead.'

'What did he want? What did he say?' Helen stared at her anxiously. 'Where is Angela? I'll ask her myself.'

'You won't. She went to bed half an hour ago,' stated the housekeeper quellingly. 'But I shouldn't worry—he wasn't on long. I think he just wanted to assure himself that everything was all right. He said he expects to be coming home next Friday.'

'Next Friday!' echoed Helen in dismay. 'But he was only going for a week.'

'I can't help that. Something must have happened to delay him,' said Mrs Gittens firmly. 'Now, you'd best get along to bed. I don't want Miss Patterson telling your uncle I'm encouraging you to stay out late.'

'It's not late.' Helen's eyes sought the clock now. 'It's only half past ten.'

'Late enough for a girl of your age,' declared Mrs Gittens tartly. 'And it's just as well Mr Heathcliffe isn't here, if you ask me. Next time you let a young man kiss you in his car, have the foresight to use a comb on your hair before coming into the house!'

Helen remembered this as she stood before her dressing table mirror a few minutes later. Her hair was a little untidy, and her mouth was bare of any lipstick. She looked as if she had been kissed, she reflected, and was amazed to find she suited the condition. Nigel's lovemaking had put colour in her cheeks, and she realised, with a pang, that only the news that Heath had rung had robbed her face of a vivid kind of beauty.

CHAPTER NINE

ANGELA was infuriatingly reticent about what Heath had said the next morning.

'I can't remember,' she said, coming down to breakfast when Helen had nearly finished, drinking her coffee slowly with an annoyingly faraway look in her eyes. 'Did you have a nice evening? Was it a good meal? I must admit your young man seemed very presentable.'

'He's not my young man,' retorted Helen shortly, and Angela's narrow brows arched.

'What else would you call him, then?' she countered. 'He's hardly a friend of the family. Heath has never even met him.'

'Is that what he said?' Helen took a calming breath. 'Heath, I mean?'

'Yes.' Angela reached for the coffee pot. 'What a pity you missed his call.'

'Did he ask where I was?' Helen probed, and Angela inclined her head. 'Naturally he wanted to know who you were out with, so I told him.'

Helen sighed. 'Did you explain the predicament I was in when I met Nigel? Did you tell him the motorbike had broken down?'

'I think he thought you should have checked the petrol tank on the bike before leaving,' essayed Angela smoothly. 'He said it was irresponsible to ride round the country without taking reasonable precautions.'

Helen hunched her shoulders, resting her elbows on the table and cupping her chin in her hands. 'I suppose you agreed with him,' she muttered, and Angela smiled.

'Well, it was rather foolhardy, wasn't it?'

'I forgot,' said Helen wearily. 'I just forgot.'

Angela lifted her slim shoulders. 'Well, perhaps Heath will have forgotten about it by the time he gets home.'

Helen wished she could be so certain, but she kept her thoughts to herself and asked instead: 'Did he say why he was going to be delayed? I thought he was coming home tomorrow.'

'Oh, I'm not sure.' Angela frowned. 'Something to do with a contract not being signed, I believe. In any case, he'll be leaving on Friday, which I assume means he'll be back in this country on Saturday morning.'

'So long?' Helen was overwhelmed by dejection, but Angela looked quite complacent.

'It will give us a little longer to get used to one another,' she remarked. 'That's what Heath wants. It's what he said. Perhaps we ought to devote the time to your appearance. You're still wearing those scruffy jeans you were wearing when we met.'

Helen shrugged. 'They're a different pair,' she declared staunchly. 'And I don't need your help. I can choose my own clothes.'

'Oh, really?' Angela's smile was frosty. 'And did you tell Mrs Marsden what Heath thought of her efforts?'

Helen didn't answer her, resting her head on one hand and drawing figure eights on the tablecloth with her nail, until Angela grew impatient. 'Perhaps your uncle's right,' she exclaimed spitefully. 'Maybe a school far away from Matlock Edge is the only answer.'

Helen's head jerked upward. 'Did Heath say that?'

'It's been on the cards all along, hasn't it?' retorted Angela obliquely. 'When your uncle asked me to come here, he expected you to make an effort to change. But you haven't, have you? And Friday's little escapade has made things worse.'

Helen caught her breath. 'All right, I won't see Nigel again.'

'Oh, no——' Angela's previously malicious expression gave way to unexpected benevolence, 'that's not what I meant at all.'

'You said Friday's little escapade,' Helen reminded her suspiciously, but Angela only lifted a placating hand.

'I meant going out without petrol, of course,' she explained swiftly. 'Meeting Nigel Fox may have been the best thing you could do.' She paused. 'After all, if Heath meets Nigel and likes him, he can't have any objections to your friendship. It's exactly what he expects of you.'

'What do you mean?' Helen was still suspicious, and Angela quickly explained.

'He can hardly accuse you of acting like a child, if you behave like an adult. Having a steady boy-friend is the first step towards marriage, and——'

'I'm not getting married!' Helen interrupted her fiercely, but Angela only continued with what she was saying as if she hadn't spoken.

'—although you may have dozens of boy-friends before you find the one you want to spend the rest of your life with, you'll be proving you're no longer a social liability.'

Helen looked doubtful. 'Aren't you worried that Heath might make you redundant?' she asked, with a trace of defensive malice, but Angela shook her head.

'Your uncle brought me here to help you, it's true, but also to act as chaperone, and I don't think he'll change his mind just because you've found yourself a boy-friend.'

Helen absorbed this in silence. So that was Angela's true function, was it? A chaperone. Giving her advice was only a sideline. Her real value was to silence those local gossips, whose greatest pleasure was to blacken Heath's character. She sighed. Since when had Heath cared what anyone said? He had often maintained that evil, like beauty, was in the eye of the beholder.

She linked her fingers tightly together. But what if Angela had got it wrong? What if their roles were reversed? What if *she* was actually the chaperone without even knowing it? What did it mean? What might it mean? That the woman Heath intended to marry should have no scandal attached to her name?

For the rest of the day Helen suffered her thoughts in silence, and on Monday morning she put her differences with Miles aside and went round to the garage. She needed to get out of the house. She needed to talk to somebody. And for all his amorous advances, Miles was still one of the best friends she'd got.

He was bent over the engine of the lawnmower when Helen strolled casually into the yard, and he gave her only a cursory glance before continuing with what he was doing.

'Hi,' she said offhandedly, coming to stand beside him. 'What are you doing?'

'What does it look like I'm doing?' retorted Miles shortly. 'What do you want, *Miss* Helen? It's some time since you came slumming round here.'

'Oh, Miles!' Helen tucked her thumbs into the belt to her jeans. 'Don't be like this. I'm sorry if I offended you, but really, I still want us to be friends.'

He looked up at her from his crouched position. 'What if I don't want to be friends with you?' he countered brusquely. 'I hear you've found yourself another sucker. Does he know he's wasting his time, too?'

She flushed. 'I don't know what you mean.'

'Sure you do.' Miles straightened, wiping the spanner he had been using against the leg of his overalls. 'It took me some time to figure it out, but I think I've got the picture now. No wonder Heath was so mad when he came upon us together! I didn't know I was trespassing on his property!'

'Miles!' Helen stared at him aghast, and the young man shrugged indifferently.

'It's true, isn't it? You are in love with your uncle, aren't you?'

'He's not my uncle, you know that,' exclaimed Helen tremulously, pushing her hands into her back hip pockets.

'So it is true,' said Miles harshly. 'Oh, Helen, he's far too old for you!'

'I don't know what you're talking about.' Helen turned abruptly away, feeling suddenly empty inside. She had thought she could still talk to Miles. But apparently he, like everyone else, had his own axe to grind.

'Yes, you do.' He came behind her, putting his hands on her shoulders and turning her resistingly to face him. 'I just wouldn't have expected it of Heath, I wouldn't. For God's sake, I thought he cared about you!'

'He does.' Helen swallowed convulsively. 'And—and you're wrong.'

'Wrong about what?' Miles looked disbelievingly.

'Heath's not interested in me. At least, only as an uncle, as you say. If you thought you read something into his attitude, you were wrong. On the contrary, he would have sent me away from Matlock, if I hadn't begged and pleaded with him to let me stay.'

'You mean the finishing school,' said Miles scornfully. 'You don't really think that was a possibility, do you?'

'Yes, I do. And it still is.' Helen wrenched herself out of his grasp and faced him indignantly. 'Oh,

Miles, you're so blind, aren't you? It's not me Heath is interested in, it's Angela Patterson!'

Miles snorted. 'The blonde bombshell!'

'Yes, the blonde bombshell!' declared Helen tautly. 'Now do you believe me?'

Miles shrugged. 'Heath has had dozens of women like her.'

She winced at his frankness, but she was not diverted. 'Not like this one,' she averred unsteadily. 'You know as well as I do that since I got old enough to understand Heath hasn't brought any women to stay at Matlock. Until now.'

Miles shook his head. 'I thought she was here to give you lessons in deportment.'

'So did I, at first. But honestly, is it feasible?' She sighed. 'She told me herself this morning that Heath had invited her here for an indefinite period. Does that sound like lessons in deportment?'

Miles hesitated. 'You really believe this?'

'Yes.'

He frowned. 'And you? What about you? I may have been wrong about Heath, but I'm damn sure I'm not wrong about you.'

'How?' Helen took a step backward.

'You are in love with him,' he said flatly. 'I don't know why I didn't think of it before. I guess I didn't want to believe it.'

'Oh, Miles . . .' Helen bent her head. 'I came here because I thought you were a friend.'

'I am a friend,' said Miles heavily. 'I'd like to say I wasn't, but we've known one another too long.' He looked at her steadily. 'That's why I hoped you'd be honest with me.'

'All right.' The words broke from her desperately. 'All right, I am in love with Heath. I guess I always have been. At least, since I was old enough to understand.'

Miles shook his head. 'Are you sure it's not just

hero-worship? He has been a powerful influence in your life, hasn't he? Are you sure you're not fantasising about someone who doesn't really exist, except in your imagination?'

'What do you mean?'

'I mean Heath's a man like other men, Helen. He has needs, appetites; he uses women, as all men use women, to satisfy their own sexual desires.'

'I know that.' Helen bent her head. 'You think I don't know what it's all about.'

'Do you?'

'Yes.'

He looked disbelieving. 'When I kissed you with something approaching passion you froze up!'

'That was different.' Helen lifted her shoulders. 'It's not like that with Heath.'

'How do you know?' he demanded forcefully. 'You'd probably freeze up just the same with him.'

'I wouldn't. I didn't.'

As soon as the words were out, she knew she had made a mistake, and Miles was not about to let her get away with it. 'What do you mean— you *didn't*?' he exclaimed, stepping nearer to her. 'Helen, has he touched you? Because if he has—I'll— I'll——'

'You'll what?' Helen's momentary dismay dispersed beneath a wave of sudden depression. 'And yes, yes, he has kissed me.' She scuffed her toe against the paving. 'But only because I *made* him do it.'

'You made him?' Miles stared at her. 'How?'

'Does it matter?' She was resigned. 'That's why I know he doesn't care about me. If he did, he would have—well, you know what I mean.'

He was appalled. 'Oh, Helen!'

'I know.' She continued to push her toe against the stone slab, avoiding his shocked gaze. 'I'm a bitch. He said so.'

'So what are you going to do?'

'Do?' She gave up her attempt to dislodge the slab, and walked disconsolately across the yard. 'I'm not going to *do* anything. What can I do, short of leaving here?'

'Is that why you're dating Nigel Fox?' asked Miles grimly. 'Are you hoping that relationship may eventually lead to your departure?'

Helen didn't jump on him as she might have done a couple of days ago. 'Who knows?' she declared bitterly. 'If Heath is serious about Angela, I couldn't stay here, that's for sure. She and I barely tolerate one another as it is.'

Miles expelled his breath impatiently. 'You could always marry me,' he said quietly. 'Or maybe I'm not good enough for you.'

'Oh, Miles!' Helen tugged his sleeve impulsively. 'Of course you're good enough for me. You're too good for me, actually.' She grimaced. 'But you know it wouldn't work. I don't love you.'

'We could work at it.'

'Is that what you want?'

'No.' Miles was honest. 'What I really want is for you to love me, but if that can't be, I'm prepared to settle for whatever is left.'

Helen touched his cheek with the back of her hand, and he caught her hand in his and raised it to his lips. 'Just remember,' he said huskily, 'I saw you before Nigel Fox!'

Nigel phoned Helen on Monday as he had promised.

At first, after her conversation with Miles, she had been tempted to refuse to see him again, but the remembrance of what Angela had said made her wary. There was always the chance that she was wrong, that Heath had not brought Angela here because he was seriously attracted to her, and if that were so, the last thing Helen wanted to do was give him any cause to reconsider the school in Geneva.

They went to the cinema in Bradford, as Nigel had suggested, and afterwards they had a supper of chicken chow mein at a Chinese restaurant. 'You know, I can never remember the difference between chow mein and chop suey,' Nigel confessed, forking bean sprouts into his mouth. 'I just know they have crispy noodles, and that's the thing I like best!'

'I love Chinese food,' said Helen, rescuing a grain of rice from the corner of her lip. 'But then, you see, I love English food, too.' She grimaced. 'Angela doesn't approve at all.'

'I imagine her appetite is rather fragile,' remarked Nigel perceptively. 'I shouldn't like you to be as thin as that. It isn't really healthy.'

Helen grimaced. 'You're very gallant.'

'No, I mean it.' He looked at her warmly. 'You're exactly right the way you are.'

'You're very good for my ego.' Helen was rueful, but Nigel's gaze didn't falter.

'You're just very good for me,' he declared, leaning across the table to squeeze her hand. 'Now, eat up. I rather fancy some pineapple fritters, don't you?'

He delivered her back to Matlock Edge soon after ten-thirty, and once again he suggested another date. 'How about coming to a party with me on Friday evening?' he invited. 'I know you said your uncle's coming back on Friday, but I promise I won't keep you out too late.'

Helen hesitated. 'Heath's not coming back until Saturday, actually,' she admitted slowly. 'Where is the party being held? I'd have to let Angela know where I was.'

'It's at the flat of a friend of mine in Harrogate,' Nigel explained, causing Helen to look doubtful. 'I know it's not exactly on the doorstep, but we'd leave for home in plenty of time.'

'Are you sure?' She was uncertain. 'It's about twenty miles to Harrogate!'

'Nineteen, actually,' said Nigel pedantically. 'But don't let that worry you. The old M.G. is quite reliable.'

Helen shook her head. 'I don't know . . .'

'Why not?'

'I don't think Heath would approve.'

'But your uncle won't be here, as you've just pointed out,' replied Nigel reasonably. 'Oh, come on, Helen! You're not a baby. You've got to strike out on your own sometime.'

'Oh, very well.' Helen gave in reluctantly, not at all sure she wouldn't live to regret it. 'But I must be back here by eleven o'clock at the latest. Do you agree?'

Nigel sighed. 'If you insist.' He looked at her wryly. 'Now, do I deserve some gratitude?'

Helen allowed him to kiss her, participating to the extent of putting her arms around his neck, but when his mouth sought the scented hollow of her throat, she drew back. 'I'm not—I don't—that is, I think I'd better go, Nigel,' she averred with determined firmness, and he traced the contours of her mouth with his finger before obediently letting her escape him.

'You're very sweet,' he said softly. 'And very sexy. I just can't believe my luck.'

'What do you mean?' Helen asked curiously, and he leant past her to the push open the door.

'I can't believe I'm the first guy to think so,' he said, though she had the suspicion that was not what he had been thinking at all. 'No wonder that uncle of yours keeps you to himself! So would I.'

Helen got out abruptly. She didn't want to be reminded of Heath just then. She didn't want to remember why she had accepted Nigel's invitation, or be forced to imagine the number of times Heath must have said something similar to a girl. She had purposely avoided ever picturing Heath with other women. Until now, it had been taboo. But Nigel's suggestive words had triggered her imagination, and suddenly she found herself facing the fact that Heath went to bed with those other females.

'Goodnight,' she said tautly, slamming the door and striding swiftly towards the house, almost as if she believed she could outstrip her thoughts, which she couldn't.

'Goodnight,' Nigel called after her, a trace of speculation in his tone, and Helen guessed he was probably wondering what he had said to upset her.

On Friday evening, she was ready and waiting when Nigel arrived. They were leaving earlier than usual, because of the distance to Harrogate, and Mrs Gittens viewed Helen's appearance critically when she came down the stairs.

'Is that new?' she asked, surveying the lacy camisole dress Helen had bought with Marion nearly two weeks ago.

'It is. Do you like it?' Helen smoothed the honey-coloured cotton over her hips with unknowingly sensuous hands. 'It's a warm evening. I shouldn't need a coat.'

'I should take a scarf with you, if you're going to ride in that sports car of Mr Fox's,' pronounced the housekeeper dourly. 'And you watch what you're doing. I'm not at all sure Mr Heathcliffe would let you go.'

'Oh, leave her alone, Mrs Gittens.' Angela's drawling voice interrupted them. 'Whatever do you think is going to happen to her? Mr Fox seems a respectable young man.'

'Mr Heathcliffe wasn't too pleased to hear she was out the other evening,' asserted the housekeeper staunchly, put out at having her authority thwarted, and Helen turned to her anxiously.

'What did he say, Mrs Gittens?' she demanded. 'I didn't know you'd told him where I was.'

'Well, of course she told him. I told him, too,' inserted Angela impatiently. 'Naturally he was disappointed that you weren't here to speak to him, but I don't recall any animosity because you had a date.'

'He wasn't pleased,' insisted Mrs Gittens. 'I've known him a lot longer than you have, Miss Patterson, if you don't mind me saying so, and I know when Mr Heathcliffe's happy about something and when he's not.'

'Oh, nonsense!' Angela made a sound of derision. 'Helen, your uncle wants you to get out and mix with people of your own age. Mrs Gittens is probably colouring her recollection of what Heath said with her own opinion. To her, you're still a little girl, but we both know you're not, don't we?'

Helen was doubtful, influenced more by Mrs Gittens' red face than by Angela's cool-eyed persuasion, but it was already too late. As she was standing there looking from one to the other of them, Nigel rang the bell, and the housekeeper went to answer the door with hollow-cheeked disapproval.

The flat where the party was being held was in a modern block near to the new conference centre. At least fifty young people were crowded into a living area not much more than twenty feet square, and in consequence they had overflowed into the hall and the bedrooms. Helen and Nigel were greeted by a thin young man in glasses, who took one look at Helen before expelling his breath in a low whistle.

'Hey, where have you been hiding all my life?' he exclaimed, eyeing her admiringly, and Nigel explained reluctantly that this was their host.

'Helen, meet Vic Boulton,' he said tolerantly. 'Vic, this is Helen Mortimer. You remember, I told you I was bringing her.'

'Oh, sure, I remember.' Vic tucked his arm possessively through hers. 'Come on, Helen, let me introduce you around. Nigel, get lost, will you?'

There followed one of the most bewildering interludes in Helen's life. She was introduced to so many people that eventually the names didn't mean a thing, and she looked around rather desperately for Nigel, wishing he would come and rescue her. With a glass of some unidentifiable liquid in one hand and an equally bizarre sandwich in the other, she felt totally isolated, and Vic's sudden departure to meet another guest left her stranded at the other side of the room.

'You can never be sure Vic's not serving grass in his sandwiches,' remarked a girl beside her, dressed all in black, with curious orange streaks in her dark hair. 'Anything to get the party rolling, that's his maxim. You want to beware of the joints they'll be passing round later.'

'Grass?' Helen looked at her sandwich suspiciously. 'He wouldn't put grass in sandwiches, would he?'

'Who knows?' The girl rolled her eyes expressively. 'I've heard he had acid at a party he gave in Kingston. Our Victor's not a nice man. Not a nice man at all.'

Helen swallowed convulsively. 'When—when you say grass, you mean—marijuana, don't you?'

The dark girl arched her brows. 'Who wants to know? Do you belong to the drugs squad, or something?'

'Of course not.' But Helen had her answer. She now knew what the joints were that the girl had mentioned earlier.

'I guess you've never been to one of Vic's parties before,' she was saying now. 'I thought you looked kind of—innocent. Who brought you?'

'Er—Nigel. Nigel Fox,' said Helen, looking about her desperately. 'I—could you tell me where the bathroom is? I'd like to use the loo.'

In the event, she dropped all her drink and the remains of her sandwich into the toilet, before examining her flushed cheeks in the mirror above the basin. Dear lord, she thought, what had she got herself into now? And how the devil was she going to get away when Nigel apparently had known what to expect?

He was waiting for her when she emerged into the corridor, and her eyes avoided his as she adjusted the strap of her dress. She had been considering leaving without his knowledge, but now that he was facing her, she knew she had to tell the truth.

'I'd like to go home,' she said, without preamble, causing him to do a double-take. 'You didn't tell me your friends used drugs. I'm sorry, but I don't want to stay.'

'What did Vic say?' exclaimed Nigel impatiently. 'Helen, you mustn't believe all his lies.'

'It wasn't Vic. It was someone else, actually,' replied Helen, sighing. 'I'm sorry, Nigel. I don't want to spoil your evening.'

'But you are spoiling it, don't you see?' He spread his hands. 'Look, no one's going to insist you smoke, if you don't want to. Just give it a bit longer, will you? The night's still young.'

Helen shook her head. 'I want to go, Nigel. I want to go now.' She was imagining what Heath would say if he ever found out, and the possibility that the party might be raided was not as outrageous as it seemed.

'Oh, Helen——'

Nigel was raking his fingers through his brown hair when the girl Helen had spoken to earlier appeared beside them. In black leather pants and jacket, and high-heeled boots complete with spurs, she was a total contrast to Nigel's clean-cut appearance, but her eyes were sympathetic when they rested on Helen.

'You leaving?' she asked, shifting her gaze to Nigel. 'I don't think your lady likes the company.'

'Was it you she's been talking to?' Nigel demanded angrily. 'Why don't you keep your mouth shut, Alanna? Helen was enjoying herself until you interfered.'

'Oh, I don't think she was.' The girl called Alanna was not put out. 'I should take her home if I were you, Nigel. She might tell your daddy, and then what would you do?'

'Oh, shut up!' Nigel snapped aggressively, and Helen was surprised at this totally new side to his character. 'If she wants to go home, then she can do so. But I'm not leaving. It's barely nine o'clock.'

Helen caught her breath. 'All right, I will,' she declared tensely, and Nigel turned scornful eyes in her direction.

'And how are you going to get home?'

'There are buses. And taxis,' replied Helen coldly. 'Don't worry about me, Nigel. I'm not entirely helpless.'

He sighed, his expression mirroring his frustration. 'Aw, hey, Helen, don't go,' he exclaimed weakly. 'I'll take you home later, like I promised. Come on, come back to the party. We'll have some fun——'

'Where do you live?' asked Alanna, as she was shaking her head, and Helen looked at her in surprise.

'Near Starforth,' she answered. 'A house called Matlock Edge, in the Pendle Valley.'

'I know it,' said Alanna, nodding. 'Okay, I'll take you home, if you like——'

'Now, wait a minute,' began Nigel indignantly. 'Helen came with me——'

'And you don't want to leave,' put in Alanna reasonably. 'Come on, Helen. You don't belong here. Nigel shouldn't have brought you, and I think he knows that now.'

'Well——'

Helen was undecided and Nigel caught her arm. 'Take no notice of her,' he ordered, giving Alanna a killing glance. 'She's only trying to ruin my evening.

Come on, give a little, can't you? You'd think I was trying to get you into bed!'

'And aren't you?' enquired Alanna coolly. 'What do you want to do, Helen? Stay or go? Make up your mind.'

'I want to go,' decided Helen firmly, releasing herself from Nigel's possessive grasp. 'Are you coming, Nigel? Or do I have to make other arrangements?'

'Go to hell!' said Nigel harshly, using an ugly epithet, and Helen's cheeks flamed as she pulled open the door and ran down the steps. Thank goodness she had found out in time, she thought weakly. Without Alanna's intervention, she might well have found herself without the will to resist any suggestion he made.

'Hey—wait!'

The other girl's voice arrested her, and she turned reluctantly as Alanna followed her down the steps of the apartment building. She wasn't at all sure she could trust her either, and she half wished she had insisted on taking a taxi.

'Do you want a lift?' Alanna joined her on the first landing, her plucked eyebrows arching interrogatively. 'Don't worry, I promise I'm quite reliable. Just so long as you don't object to riding on the pillion.'

Helen's eyes widened. 'You've got a motorbike?'

'Dressed like this, did you think I'd drive a car?' Alanna gave her a wry smile. 'Look, I know you're probably not used to motorbikes, but you'd be quite safe, believe me.'

'Not used——' Helen broke off to shake her head. 'Alanna, I have a motorbike of my own. It's not a big machine, only a little one, actually. But Miles, that's my uncle's mechanic, he's sharpened it up for me, and it can really go.'

'You don't say!' Alanna was clearly delighted. 'Come on then, I'll show you my piece of metal. Here was I thinking you were fragile and feminine, and you're really just another rocker, like me!'

Alanna's motorbike was a sleek Suzuki, almost a thousand horse-power, with a capacity well beyond the limit of current speed limits. She was evidently very proud of it, and Helen could understand why, her own modest model fading into insignificance beside the more powerful machine.

'We'll borrow one of these,' said Alanna, filching a helmet for Helen to wear from the motorbike parked beside her own. 'Right. Are we ready? Okay, let's go!'

It was an exhilarating, if rather chilly, ride home. Although the night was warm, they were moving through the air at such a pace that Helen's arms were soon frozen, and they remained clamped to Alanna's leather jacket as much by the fact that she could scarcely move them as by any fear of falling off.

The motorbike roared through the lodge gates soon after half-past nine, and Helen could imagine old Jenkins rushing to his window to see if they were being invaded by a crowd of punk rockers. It sped up through the park like a bat out of hell, and when they reached the drive gates, Helen hardly had the strength to extricate herself and climb down to open it.

'You okay?' asked Alanna, as Helen climbed back on again, and the younger girl nodded.

'Just a bit cold,' she admitted, hugging her shivering body, and Alanna opened the throttle to cover the last few yards.

'Are you sure this is where you live?' she asked, as Helen climbed down again at the front door, and her companion smiled.

'Yes. It's nice, isn't it? Do you want to come in for a cup of tea?'

The shaft of light that suddenly illuminated them as they stood there on the drive came from the abrupt opening of the front door. The stream of radiance was only interrupted by the figure of the man who stood in the doorway, and Helen's lips parted as she identified that lean frame.

'*Heath!*' she exclaimed disbelievingly. 'Oh, Heath, I thought you weren't coming back until tomorrow!' She clasped her hands together uncertainly as she looked from his shadowy outline to that of Alanna. 'How—how fortunate that I've got back early.'

Heath came down the steps with Mrs Gittens hovering at his back, and Alanna raised mocking brows in Helen's direction. 'No wonder you wanted to get back,' she remarked for Helen's ears only, as Heath stepped out of the shadows. 'With that at home, who'd want to waste time with Nigel Fox?'

Helen gave a nervous smile, but she wasn't really listening. Now that she could see Heath's face, she was able to see his expression, and it did not augur well; it did not augur well at all.

'I thought you said she went out in a sports car,' Heath enquired of Mrs Gittens, and Helen, on the point of rushing towards him and throwing herself into his arms by way of a greeting, froze to the spot.

'She did, Mr Heathcliffe. I saw her myself,' Mrs Gittens assured him worriedly, and Helen's spirits sank as Heath's dark gaze was turned on her.

'I can explain——' she began helplessly, and Alanna re-started the engine of the Suzuki.

'Time for me to go, sweetie,' she said, taking the spare helmet from Helen's unresisting fingers. 'I'll have that tea some other time,' she added. 'I can see that right now I'm not exactly welcome.'

'No, wait——'

Helen would have stepped in front of her had Heath not already done so, and Alanna's tyres screamed in the gravel as she endeavoured to control the bike.

'I want to have a word with you,' Heath grated, his dark features grim and unyielding, and Alanna grimaced behind her mask as she made a swift evasion.

' 'Bye, Helen,' she called, as the motorbike accelerated swiftly down the drive, and Helen was glad she had left the gate open as the bike's tail-lights swiftly disappeared. It had been kind of Alanna to bring her home, and Heath's behaviour had been far from reasonable. He might at least have listened to their explanation before behaving like some avenging angel, and she turned to him rather mutinously, aware that the homecoming she had been looking forward to had been abruptly spoiled. Things hadn't changed, she thought miserably. He was just as overbearing now as he had been before he went away, and her hopes that his absence might have made him think more fondly of her were evidently doomed from the outset.

'Oh, Helen!' It was Mrs Gittens who noticed how the girl was shivering, and putting a hand out to touch her arm, she gave a scandalised exclamation. 'She's frozen!' she declared, looking appealingly at her employer, and Heath stepped back abruptly and gestured towards the house.

'You'd better go inside,' he said, without expression. 'I'll go and shut the gate. I assume it was left open, or your friend would have killed himself!'

Helen opened her mouth to contradict him, then closed it again. Why should she defend herself to him? she thought bitterly. He was always prepared to believe the worst of her, so let him go on doing so. Mrs Gittens was right. She was cold, and empty, and more defeated now than she had ever felt before.

CHAPTER TEN

To her relief, Angela was not about as Helen made her way upstairs to her room. Instead she was able to reach the security of her apartments undeterred, with only Mrs Gittens' clucking presence for company.

'Riding home on a motorcycle without a coat!' she declared disapprovingly, going straight into Helen's bathroom and turning on the taps. 'It'll be a wonder if you haven't caught pneumonia. Whatever happened to the car? Don't tell me you had an accident!'

'Oh, no, nothing like that.' Helen sighed wearily, too depressed to prevaricate. 'That wasn't Nigel who brought me home. He—he wanted to stay on at the party.'

'I see.' Mrs Gittens added liquid salts to the water, their aromatic perfume scenting the steamy air. 'I must admit I was surprised to see you back so early. What went wrong? Did you have a fall-out or something?'

'Or something,' agreed Helen carelessly, perching on the rim of the bath. 'Is this absolutely necessary, Mrs Gittens? Surely a hot drink would have served the purpose.'

'A summer cold is the worst kind,' stated the housekeeper firmly. 'You do as I say and get into this hot water. I don't want an invalid on my hands for the next week.'

'Oh—all right.' Obediently Helen stood up and reached for the laces of the camisole. 'But don't let Heath come up here, please. Tell him I'll speak to him in the morning.'

'Since when have I been able to tell your uncle what

to do?' asked Mrs Gittens drily, gathering the girl's hair in her hands and securing it on top of her head with some hairpins, as she had used to do when she was a little girl. 'Well, I'll do my best,' she added, as Helen stepped out of her dress, and gathered the rest of her clothes together before leaving her to soak.

The bath was wonderfully warming, and by the time Helen emerged from the water, she felt infinitely better. Drying herself with one of the fluffy pink towels, she felt enormously grateful to Alanna for bringing her home, and she wished she had thought to ask her name so that she could thank her again.

Mrs Gittens appeared with a mug of hot chocolate as Helen was tying the cord of her silk wrapper about her, and she viewed the girl's appearance with evidently more approval. 'At least you've lost that pinched look you had when you came home,' she remarked, setting the mug down on the bedside table. 'Now, you get into bed. You can have an early night.'

Helen sighed. 'In a minute, Mrs Gittens. What did Heath say? Is he very angry? What time did he get back?'

The housekeeper hesitated. 'I suppose he got back about two hours ago,' she declared, answering her last question first. 'His flight from Uruguay was delayed by several hours, otherwise he'd have been home this afternoon.

'But I thought Angela said he wouldn't be back until tomorrow.'

'I believe that was his original intention,' said Mrs Gittens, frowning. 'But apparently his business was finished and he wanted to get back.' She shrugged. 'It couldn't be helped.'

Helen bent her head. 'He is angry, isn't he?'

'You don't need me to tell you that,' retorted Mrs Gittens flatly. 'For heaven's sake, if you'd come home with Mr Fox it would have been bad enough, but on the back of some strange man's motorbike——'

'It wasn't—he wasn't—I mean, it was a girl, not a man,' said Helen reluctantly.

'The motorcyclist?' Mrs Gittens was incredulous. 'You mean that leather-clad individual was female?'

'Yes.' Helen looked at her defensively. 'It was kind of her to bring me.'

The housekeeper shook her head. 'I think you've got some explaining to do, young lady. To begin with, why didn't Mr Fox bring you home, if that was what you wanted?'

Helen shrugged. 'Does it matter? I'm home now. How or why isn't important.'

'I don't think your uncle would agree with you,' remarked the housekeeper severely, and Helen looked at her anxiously.

'But he's not going to cause a fuss tonight, is he?' she asked desperately. 'You did ask him to wait until tomorrow morning, didn't you?'

'Well, I gave him the message,' agreed Mrs Gittens briefly. 'But whether he chooses to take notice of it or not is not really my business.'

After Mrs Gittens had gone, Helen sat down on the side of the bed and picked up the mug of chocolate. But the thick sweet liquid was not appealing now that her temperature was back to normal, and she put the beaker down again and stared unhappily into space.

Perhaps it would have been better if she had allowed Heath to come and see her this evening after all, she reflected miserably. As it was, she had the prospect of a restless night ahead of her, and the uneasy conviction that leaving their encounter until the morning could only worsen an already critical situation. She ought to have explained the circum- stances of her being brought home on a motorbike to him, she realised belatedly, and explained that Alanna was not another doubtful entanglement. Allowing him to go on thinking that the other girl had been a boy had been just another piece of foolishness, and she could imagine Heath's irritation over her apparent lack of responsibility.

She sighed, getting up from the bed to walk disconsolately over to the window. Drawing the curtain aside, she looked out on to the moonlit slopes of Jacob's Hollow, and reflected rather bitterly that without Angela Patterson's company as a deterrent, nothing would have kept Heath from demanding an explanation tonight. In addition, the other girl's presence prevented Helen from going downstairs and precipitating their confrontation, and she allowed the curtain to fall into place again with unconcealed frustration.

Of course, she mused, she could wait until Heath came up to bed and speak to him then. If she went straight to his room, as soon as he came upstairs, she could speak to him before he started to get undressed, and that would solve the problem of waiting until tomorrow. It would also save having to avoid Angela's unwanted audience, and she looked at the clock consideringly, estimating how long she might have to wait.

She heard Angela come up to bed soon after eleven, and she waited with some trepidation for Heath's heavier tread. Now that the moment was fast approaching, she was having second thoughts, but compunction, and her uneasy conscience, would not allow her to change her mind. It had to be faced sooner or later, she told herself severely. Who knows, Heath might even show some admiration for her, for having shouldered her responsibilities.

The ticking of her clock became irritatingly persistent in the silence of her room. It seemed to be forcing her to keep looking at it, and she had to steel herself from staring at the slow-moving pointers. Half past eleven came and went, and then a quarter to twelve; but still Heath didn't come upstairs, and Helen shifted her weight from one foot to the other with increasing regularity. What was he doing? she asked herself. Why didn't he come? And then again, more anxiously: had something happened to him? Could he possibly be ill?

Realising she wouldn't sleep until she found out, she pushed her feet into fluffy mules and opened her bedroom door. The hall outside was quiet. There was no sound of Heath coming up to bed. With a little shrug, she closed her door behind her and hurried along to the landing, descending the stairs silently. Her heart was beating erratically as she hesitated in the hall below, not knowing exactly where she might find him. But there was a strip of light under the library door, and she guessed that was where he must be.

She was tempted to knock, but she had never knocked at the library door before, and taking her courage into her hands, she turned the handle. The door swung inwards on oiled hinges, revealing the lamplit room beyond, and her heart palpitated wildly as she saw Heath gazing at her from the depths of his armchair.

For a moment there was silence: Heath seemingly unmoved at seeing her, and Helen too bemused by her own nervousness to make any comment. But as her eyes took in the glass hanging carelessly from Heath's hand, and half empty bottle of brandy at his side, her feelings clarified, and she shook her head reprovingly as she advanced into the room.

'What do you want?'

Heath's harsh enquiry brought her abruptly to a halt, and she cast about hurriedly for something to say. 'I was concerned about you,' she declared. 'I didn't hear you come up to bed, and I was worried in case anything had happened to you. What are you doing sitting down here at midnight? You must be tired. Mrs Gittens said your plane was delayed.'

'What's it to you?' Heath levered himself up into a sitting position from the slumping sprawl he had previously adopted. 'Go to bed, Helen. We'll have our discussion in the morning. Right now, I'm not in the mood for idle chatter.'

She gasped. 'I didn't come down here to indulge in idle chatter,' she protested. 'As—as a matter of fact, I came to explain about what happened earlier. I didn't want you to worry about me, but I see now that you haven't.'

Heath expelled his breath heavily, running one hand inside the unbuttoned neckline of his shirt and massaging his chest wearily. 'It's too late now to start enumerating the rights and wrongs of your behaviour, Helen,' he said, dropping his empty glass on to the fireside table. 'Like I said before, go to bed. I don't have the patience to deal with you this evening.'

Helen sighed. 'But I want to talk now,' she exclaimed. 'I don't want to go to bed with this hanging over me. I'm sorry if I've left it so late, but I was waiting for Angela to go to bed. I didn't want to talk to you with her present. What we have to say is better said in private.'

'Oh, I agree.' He pushed himself up from his chair to regard her dourly. 'What I have to say to you is for your ears only. But l suggest you leave it until the morning anyway. I'm not really fit to argue with you tonight.'

'Because you've been drinking.' Helen's lips twisted. 'I didn't know you went in for secret drinking, Heath.'

'I don't.' His jaw hardened perceptibly. 'But now and then the occasion warrants it, and this was one of those times.'

She hesitated. 'Because of me?'

Heath inclined his head. 'Maybe.' He swayed a little unsteadily on his feet. 'You must admit, you do try my patience.'

She looked at him a moment longer, and then turned and determinedly closed the door. 'That's why I wanted to talk to you,' she explained diffidently. 'I knew you could only be thinking the worst.'

He regarded her enigmatically. 'You mean I shouldn't?' he enquired sardonically. 'Forgive me, but when my niece goes out for the evening with a man whose reputation is well known in the district, and then returns home with yet another man, of equally dubious character, I find it difficult to see any virtue in either of those occurences.'

Helen caught her breath. 'What do you mean? Does—does Nigel have a reputation?'

'You don't know?'

'No.' She stared at him. 'How could I? I didn't know him until just over a week ago. How am I supposed to know what his reputation is?'

'Perhaps you should pay more attention to what I say,' retorted Heath harshly. 'Instead of doing your utmost to infuriate me.'

'I wasn't. I didn't.' Helen spread her hands helplessly. 'Oh, what does it matter anyway? You never listen to me.'

Heath bent and picked up the bottle of brandy, examining its contents broodingly, and she took the opportunity to go on: 'And—and it wasn't another man who brought me home,' she got out jerkily. 'It was a girl—Alanna somebody or other. I didn't get her surname. I just was grateful for the lift.'

Heath lifted his eyes from the brandy and looked at her disbelievingly. 'You mean the creature who tried to run me down was a woman?'

'She didn't try to run you down. You stepped into

her path,' retorted Helen defensively. 'And yes, her name is Alanna, as I've said. She was very kind to me.'

His mouth curled. 'Really?'

'Yes, really. And—and if you weren't so goddamned stubborn, you'd appreciate it too,' exclaimed Helen unevenly. 'It isn't everyone who'd drive forty miles out of their way just to help a fellow human being. I was really thankful she was there. Without her, I'd have had to find a bus—or a taxi.'

'And why couldn't Fox bring you home?' demanded Heath, setting the bottle down on the table beside his glass. 'It was Fox you went with, wasn't it?'

'Yes.' Helen lifted her shoulders unhappily. 'He—he didn't want to come.'

'You mean he didn't want to leave the party?'

'That's right.' Helen was offhand. 'It—it was rather early. And petrol is expensive.'

He steadied himself and took a couple of steps forward. 'Perhaps you'd better tell me the real reason why he didn't bring you home,' he said, supporting himself against the side of the desk. 'I assume you had a row. What was it about? Did you suddenly discover that he intended to take you to bed?'

'No!' Helen exclaimed indignantly. 'No, it was nothing like that.'

'Then what was it like?' asked Heath incisively. 'If it wasn't sex, what could it be? I'd have gambled on its being something of the sort.'

Helen could feel the colour creeping up her cheeks, and she hastily tried to explain it away. 'Well, I suppose it was. A bit permissive, I mean,' she mumbled, fiddling with the cord of her wrapper. 'I didn't want to get involved in all that kissing and stuff. That's why I wanted to come home.'

'Was it?' Heath didn't sound very convinced, and Helen darted a glance up at his dark face. In spite of the amount of alcohol he had consumed, he was very far from being drunk, and she wondered how he would have reacted if he hadn't been as sober.

'You know what these parties are like, Heath,' she protested, even though she herself had not known until tonight. 'People drink too much, they get too—too——'

'—fresh?'

'Yes. No! Oh, that's not what I meant, and you know it.' She sighed. 'Can't you just accept that I didn't like what was going on? I came home, didn't I?'

'As you say.' Heath's thick lashes narrowed his eyes. 'I wonder what was going on, though. Strip poker? Blue videos? Drugs?'

Helen caught her breath. 'Heath, stop it!'

'Why?' He straightened away from the desk. 'Have I hit the nail on the head? It's one of those, isn't it? Let me guess—drugs!'

Her mouth quivered. 'You think you know everything, don't you?'

'When my niece gets herself involved in the drug scene, I think I have a right to be angry,' retorted Heath grimly. 'For God's sake, Helen, he was probably hoping to get you high. Compared to the amount of alcohol you're used to drinking, marijuana could be lethal!'

'You'd know, of course,' she burst out bitterly. 'I suppose you've had experience.'

'Considerably more than you, by the sound of it,' replied Heath crisply. 'What do you want me to say, Helen? That I approve of you making friends with addicts?'

'They're not addicts.' Helen sighed. 'At least, I don't think so.'

'But you don't know.'

'No.' She bent her head. 'Like I say, as soon as I found out, I said I wanted to come home. Nigel—Nigel said it was too early.'

'*Nigel!*' Heath's tone was scathing. 'How the hell could you have got involved with Nigel Fox? My God, I go away for a few days, and when I come back I find you're associating with junkies!'

'That's not true!'

'You mean—Nigel—wasn't going to imbibe?' Heath was disbelieving.

'I don't know. He said something about cigarettes——'

'Joints!' he interceded contemptuously.

'—but I didn't see him with any.'

Heath swore softly and shook his head. 'You're totally irresponsible, aren't you?'

'Because I made a mistake——'

'Because you made several mistakes,' he grated grimly. 'Not least in letting Fox pick you up in the first place. Wait until I see Ormerod! He should have made sure the tank of the bike was filled. If you hadn't got yourself stranded, you'd never have got into tonight's difficulties.'

'It wasn't Miles' fault.' Helen looked at him mutinously. 'And nothing happened. What's the matter? Don't you trust me?'

'Can I?' He stepped nearer to her, and her breathing quickened at the awareness of his brown skin only inches from her hands.

'You know you can,' she got out chokingly.

'Even when you disobey my orders.'

'What orders?' Helen looked up at him, and his eyes narrowed as he surveyed her puzzled face.

'Last week,' he said, his wine-scented breath stirring the tumbled curls on her forehead. 'When I phoned last week, Angela knew how I felt about Nigel Fox. Didn't she relay that message to you? Didn't she tell you I disapproved?'

Helen shook her head. 'No . . .'

'But she did tell you I rang?'

'Mrs Gittens told me actually. Angela—Angela was in bed when I got back.'

'Really?'

'Yes, really.' Helen moistened her dry lips, the pink tip of her tongue unknowingly provocative. 'I wasn't particularly late. It was only about half-past ten. I—I spoke to her in the morning, and we talked about your call then.'

Heath tipped his head back, but his eyes didn't leave hers. 'And what did she say?'

'Well——' Helen was nervous suddenly. 'Nothing about you disapproving of Nigel.'

'Perhaps I didn't make my feelings clear enough,' he declared flatly.

'It's more likely that she wanted me to get into trouble again,' Helen contradicted him fiercely. 'She said if I had a boy-friend, you might start to regard me as an adult.'

He inclined his head towards her. 'Now why should she say that?'

'You tell me.' Helen's eyes were fixed on the fine dark whorls of hair that were visible above the opened neckline of his shirt. 'Perhaps she's jealous.'

'Jealous?' he echoed harshly. 'Angela has no reason to be jealous.'

'Then perhaps you should tell her that,' said Helen tensely. 'She—she told me why you'd really brought her here.'

'And why was that?' he asked distantly.

'To—to be a chaperone,' said Helen at once. 'Or maybe I'm the chaperone, who knows?'

'What's that supposed to mean?'

Heath was regarding her bleakly, and Helen realised she had gone too far to draw back now. 'Oh, I should have thought it was obvious,' she declared, lifting her slim shoulders in a careless gesture. 'Angela's a very attractive girl. Not quite up to your usual standard, perhaps, but acceptable nonetheless. There was no need to invent an occupation for her—I would have understood. I may be naïve in some ways, but after living with you for more than fourteen years, I have learned the facts of life!'

Heath's hand curled round the back of her neck with the speed of a rattlesnake. 'What did you say?'

'You heard what I said,' protested Helen, shocked by his unexpected aggression, but trying hard not to show it. 'And—and you're hurting me!'

'I can hurt a lot more than this,' retorted Heath, his fingers imprisoning her throat in a vice-like grip. 'Since when do you think you have had the right to speak to me in that patronising tone? My God, I should break your bloody neck!'

She looked up at him defensively. 'You're not in love with Angela, then?

'In love with Angela?' His mouth twisted impatiently. 'Of course, I'm not in love with Angela. For God's sake, where did you get that idea?'

'You like her.'

'She's all right,' Heath shrugged indifferently.

'You always have more time for her than you do for me.'

He swore. 'No, I don't.'

'You think I'm a nuisance,' persisted Helen tremulously. 'Before you went away, you even said you felt sorry for me.'

'Sorry for myself perhaps,' muttered Heath abruptly, releasing her. 'Hell, I think you'd better go to bed, Helen.' He steadied himself with an effort. 'Like I said, I'm in no state to have this kind of conversation with you tonight. I'm not entirely sober and you're much too—too——'

'—desirable?' she breathed huskily, and his lips twisted.

'Vulnerable,' he declared grimly. 'Go to bed, Helen.

I'll overlook what happened this evening. Just—go to bed.'

Her lips parted. Heath's words were strange, unexpected, disturbing in the unspoken things they hinted. Was it possible? Was it credible? Did Heath really find her attractive after all? Was that why he had released her so abruptly? Because he was aware of his own susceptibility?

Hesitating, she ventured: 'You're not still angry with me, are you, Heath?'

'No.' He spoke flatly.

'You've forgiven me?'

He sighed. 'I've said so, haven't I?'

'Then why are you sending me to bed?' she asked softly, taking a step towards him, and he turned to look at her tormentedly as she hovered at his elbow.

'Isn't one experience enough for one evening?' he demanded harshly. 'Helen, I'm asking you for the last time—leave me, please. I don't want to hurt you, but I may not be able to prevent myself.'

She quivered. 'Nothing you did could hurt me, Heath,' she breathed, feeling the tension like a tangible force between them. 'But if you want me to say goodnight, then naturally, I will.'

'Dear God, Helen——'

He closed his eyes against the provocative curve of her breast, just visible above the lapels of her wrapper, and she took an unsteady breath before turning away. Heath always had control of the situation, she thought painfully. She was wasting her time imagining that she might ever persuade him to do anything against his will.

She had reached the door when he came after her, and her fingers fell nervously from the handle as his fists slammed against the panels. Turning, her back against its solid frame, she faced him steadily, and he supported his weight on either side of her, looking down into her slightly flushed features with narrowed disturbing eyes.

'I suppose you want to go now,' he challenged her grimly, but she shook her head. 'Then you should,' he added, his thumb probing lightly at her collar. 'And I should let you.'

She drew a deep breath. 'Would you?' she tendered huskily, her fingers brushing the fine silk of his shirt, and she felt the flesh tense beneath her featherlight touch.

'Helen——' he groaned, his eyes moving urgently over her face. 'You don't know what you're doing——'

'I think I do,' she countered softly. 'Aren't you going to kiss me? That is what you're thinking about, isn't it?'

Heath's harsh laugh was self-derisive. 'Oh, yes,' he agreed harshly, his eyes moving possessively down over the rounded curves of her body, 'that is what I'm thinking about. You're right. That, and the awareness that I'm rapidly going out of my skull——'

When his head bent towards her, Helen's lips parted eagerly, but Heath's lips sought the hollow dimple below her left ear. His tongue explored the tiny depression, moving on to search the clefts and contours of her ear itself, his warm breath moistening her skin and causing little *frissons* of anticipation to slide along her spine. She had never known such sensuous sensations in her life, and her shoulder arched involuntarily to meet his probing mouth.

His lips moved on, over the heightened colour in her cheeks to the flickering uncertainty of her eyes, closing each one with kisses, and causing vivid images of his dark face to dance inside her eyelids. Each delicate caress awakened a mass of quivering senses, arousing her deepest emotions; each succeeding salutation leaving her weak and longing for more.

By the time his lips found her mouth, Helen was desperate for his touch. Her mouth opened to his like a flower to the sun, and his experimental restraint gave way to a searching sensuality. His lips no longer teased, they possessed, and when he lowered his weight against her, Helen felt as if she was drowning in the taste and the smell and the feel of him. But it was a pleasurable sensation, a thrilling intimacy to feel the swollen muscles between his legs hard against her stomach, and her senses swam dizzily as he slid the silk wrapper from her shoulder.

'Are you wearing anything under this?' he muttered unsteadily; his hands moving up from her waist to the pointed arousal of her breasts, and Helen shook her head.

'I was going to bed,' she said huskily. 'You know I don't wear anything when I go to bed. You've seen me.'

'Not like this,' he told her thickly. 'Never like this!' and pressing the silk gown down from her shoulders, his hands sought possession of her body.

She had never had a man touch her like this before. She had never felt a man's hard fingers moulding her firm beauty, filling his hands with her fullness and her softness, feeling her nipples crest into hard peaks against his palms. With trembling fingers, she separated the buttons of his shirt and pressed herself against him, her emotions roused to fever pitch by the hair-roughened abrasion of his taut skin.

His hands were at her waist suddenly, loosening the restraining cord and allowing her robe to fall unheeded to her feet. Now when he reached for her, his hands were on her hips, lifting her yielding body to meet his thrusting masculinity, making her aware of how impeding his garments were.

'I want you,' he said against her hair, his breathing as tortured as hers was now, his hands holding her against him with urgent intensity. 'Dear God, I've got to have you. You're tearing me apart!'

Helen's answer was to reach up for his mouth, her bare arms around his neck driving him on to that

ultimate surrender. With a groan of anguish, he dealt
ruthlessly with his own clothes, kicking his boots and
socks aside as he lifted her into his arms.

He laid her on the long sofa below the windows,
where she had sat the evening after he had delivered the
spanking, listening to his and Angela's conversation.
Now there was no conversation, only an irresistible
need, and the overpowering need to assuage it.

'I'm going to hurt you,' he muttered, cupping her
face in his hands and parting her lips with his thumb.
'Forgive me,' he added, covering her mouth with his,
and the involuntary cry she uttered was stifled by his
passionate caress.

For a moment, she panicked, the full realisation of
what she was doing—of what she had done—causing
her to buck against his crushing weight. But the
probing sensuality of his mouth against her parted lips
was intoxicating, and the awareness of their undeniable
intimacy turned all her limbs to water.

When he started to move, she wanted to protest,
half afraid he was going to leave her, but he didn't.
Instead, he covered her face with urgent kisses, and
his lean frame incited a rhythm she was powerless to
resist. What began as an instinctive response to his
movements soon became a compulsive lure, a throb-
bing, expanding need inside her, that only Heath
could fulfil. She didn't know what he was doing to her
she didn't know where he was taking her, but her
limbs grew moist and her scalp felt damp as she
surged to meet his demands.

The sudden satiation was unbelievable, a shattering
fragmentation of herself into Heath and Heath into
her, and he slumped heavily against her, his shuddering
body eloquent that he had experienced it, too.

'Oh—I love you,' she breathed, turning her face
against his neck, and although he didn't answer her,
she was content that he must feel the same. It was

fantastic, she thought disbelievingly; that Heath should have held out for so long. She was meant for him, they were meant for each other, and they must never ever be parted again.

The heavy rhythm of his breathing grew deeper, and turning her head, she saw to her surprise that he was asleep. The arduous journey he had made, added to the amount of alcohol he had consumed, plus the exertion of their making love had all combined to exhaust him, she reflected tenderly. What a pity they weren't in bed. He could have slept until the morning.

'Heath,' she whispered, endeavouring to wriggle free of him. 'Heath, wake up. You can't stay here.' But no amount of shaking would dislodge him, and although she disliked having to do so, she was forced to extricate herself from beneath him.

He slumped on the couch where she had been without stirring, and she crossed the room quickly to pick up her wrapper. She picked up Heath's clothes, too, folding them carefully before placing them on a chair, and then regarded him anxiously as she considered her options.

Eventually she came to a decision, and letting herself out of the library, she hurried back up the stairs. Heath's room was empty, his bed turned down as Mrs Gittens had left it, and gathering up the embossed cream quilt, Helen carried it back downstairs.

Once Heath was covered with the quilt, she had no further reason to linger. If only he hadn't fallen asleep like that, she thought regretfully. If only they had had a chance to talk together and discuss what they were going to do. As it was, she felt lost and a little tearful, and reluctant to return to her own empty bed . . .

It was early when Helen went downstairs the next morning, but her hasty glance into the library proved superfluous. Heath had gone; his clothes, and the quilt she had used to cover him, had all disappeared, and the room was as unoccupied as it generally was at this hour.

Frowning, she made her way to the morning room, only to halt in surprise at the sight of the man she was looking for seated casually at the table. Heath was eating toast, the morning's paper propped against a jar of marmalade, the remains of a cooked breakfast pushed carelessly to one side.

Helen was astonished that he was up so early when he must still be suffering from jet-lag, but she was delighted to see him. Without waiting for him to greet her, she went quickly across the room to his side, sliding her arms round his neck from behind and bestowing a warm kiss on his ear.

'For God's sake, Helen!' His reaction made her wonder if he hadn't observed her after all, and had hoped she would go away again. 'What the hell do you think you're doing? Do you want Mrs Gittens to think I've taken leave of my senses?'

His hands about her wrists extricated himself, and he got abruptly to his feet, putting the width of his chair between them. His face was dark with anger, eloquent of the tight rein he was having to put on himself, Helen decided, and she gazed at him uncomprehendingly as he continued to keep her at bay.

'It doesn't matter,' she exclaimed. 'It doesn't matter what Mrs Gittens thinks, does it? After today, she'll know all about us, won't she? I imagine she'll be surprised, but not entirely outraged.'

Heath's mouth tightened. 'What do you mean— after today? What has today got to do with it?'

'Well, we'll be telling her, won't we?' declared Helen reasonably. 'She'll have to know sooner or later. It's not a secret, is it?'

His hands clenched on the back of the carved chair. 'What's not a secret, Helen?'

She bent her head. 'Don't make me say it, Heath. You know what I'm talking about. Stop pretending you don't.'

Heath drew in his breath wearily, and then turned away. 'Oh, yes,' he said harshly. 'Yes, I know. I wish to God I didn't, but that's hardly relevant now, is it?'

She felt as if someone had just delivered a sharp blow to her solar plexus. 'You—you wish to God you didn't?' she echoed faintly. 'I'm—I'm afraid I don't understand . . .'

'You must,' said Heath heavily, turning to face her from some feet away. 'You can't believe that what happened last night is in any way forgivable? For God's sake, Helen, why did you let me do it?'

'Why did I——?'

'Oh, yes, yes.' Heath raked his scalp with his fingers frustratedly. 'I know I can't blame you exactly. It was all my doing. But you knew it was wrong. Why on earth didn't you get the hell out of there while you had the chance?'

Helen gulped. 'I didn't want to go, Heath. I—I love you. For me, it was a marvellous experience. Why are you spoiling everything now, when——'

'Spoiling? *Spoiling*?' he repeated savagely. 'The spoiling was done last night. I behaved like an oaf, a barbarian—a drunken brute, without the sense to satisfy my baser needs with someone who knew what it was all about!'

Helen's hands were trembling so much, they would hardly push into the narrow pockets of her jeans, but she forced them to do so, not wanting Heath to see how badly shocked she was. A small part of her brain kept insisting that this could not be happening, that it was some bad nightmare she was having, and any minute she would wake up in the pink and gold luxury of her own room. But the major part of her consciousness was aware of what was going on. The

major part of her consciousness was telling her that
Heath had not intended to make love to her, that it
had been a combination of circumstances that had
driven him to do what he had, and that without the
lateness of the hour, the amount of alcohol he had
consumed, and her state of undress—her actual
mistake in being there, in fact—he would never have
allowed her to see that side of his nature.

'Stop looking at me like that!'

Heath's fists clenched as he met her helpless gaze,
and Helen shook her head in bemused disillusion. 'I
don't know what to say,' she said, her eyes darting
away from his. 'I've obviously made a terrible
mistake.'

'No,' he said violently. 'I made the mistake, Helen.
It was all my fault. But that doesn't alter the situation,
or reassure me about the state of your emotional
development.'

She gasped. 'What do you mean?'

'I mean——' Heath broke off awkwardly, and then
went on harshly: 'It seems to me, you don't understand the implications of what happened last night.'

'The implications?'

'Yes.' He ran a hand round the back of his neck,
where the ash-blond lightness of his hair brushed the
collar of his dark jacket. 'Look, this isn't easy for me
to say—I'm not your mother—but,' he paused, 'what
would have happened if it had been—Nigel Fox or—
or Miles Ormerod who tried to seduce you?'

'They wouldn't have succeeded,' declared Helen
unsteadily. 'I don't love Nigel Fox or Miles Ormerod.'

'Oh, for God's sake, you don't love me!' grated
Heath angrily. 'You—you just think you do because
I'm the first man to—to make you feel——'

'That's not true,' she interrupted him fiercely,
unable to listen to any more without defending herself.
'You surely can't believe I'd let any other man touch

me? For heaven's sake, Heath, what do you think I am?'

'You're crazy! he muttered, but there was an unmistakable trace of uncertainty in his voice now, and Helen responded to it.

'I'm not,' she exclaimed. 'I've told you—I love you. I could no more have stopped you making love to me than—than I could change the days of the week.'

'Oh, *God*!' He shook his head in resigned defeat. 'I suppose I should have suspected you would say that.'

'Why not?' Helen took a hesitant step towards him. 'It's the truth, Heath. Why won't you admit it? What happened between us, it—it was beautiful! I couldn't let anyone else—do that.'

'Well, I could—and *have*,' he declared grimly. 'Helen, you may not be crazy, but this situation certainly is. I am *not* in love with you. I care about you, of course. You're in my care, such as it is,' he added derisively. 'But what happened last night was— a mistake, as you suggested a few moments ago. I must have been out of my mind. It was not marvellous—or beautiful; it was just a sexual experience, and God forgive me, my only consolation is that your first experience was not the traumatic affair it might have been with someone else.'

Her jaw quivered defensively. 'Oh—you're good, I'll give you that,' she burst out painfully. 'You actually made me believe you cared.'

'God, I did care,' retorted Heath roughly. 'But that's no excuse, is it? What we have to decide now is what we're going to do with you.'

She blinked. 'To do with me?' she echoed. 'Why, nothing, I suppose. We just go on as before——'

'*No!*'

Heath was vehement, and her stomach churned unpleasantly. 'What do you mean? What else is there to do?' Her lips twisted. 'I promise I won't tell Angela, if that's what you're afraid of.'

'I don't give a damn about Angela,' replied Heath flatly. 'Angela will have to go.'

'To go?' She stared at him apprehensively.

'Yes, to go,' he agreed, pacing across the room restlessly. 'If you go to Geneva, there'll be no use for her here.'

Her cry of protest was heartfelt. 'But you can't do that!' she exclaimed. 'You said—you brought Angela here——'

'—to try and improve a deteriorating situation,' he interrupted her harshly. 'That hasn't happened, has it? I won't bother to specify each individual incident, but all in all, Angela's presence has not proved a huge success, has it?'

Helen's mouth was too dry to speak, and he went on inexorably. 'I'm sorry it has to be like this, but I can't say I haven't had fair warning. My mother was of the opinion——'

'*Your mother!*' she overrode him tearfully. 'Since when has your mother had anything good to say about me? Oh, Heath, don't do this! Don't send me away! I'll die if you send me to Geneva!'

CHAPTER ELEVEN

OF course she wouldn't, she *couldn't* die to order, Helen reflected miserably, staring out at Manchester's rain-wet streets. Even though she had wished desperately that she could; even though she had given up eating and drinking, and sleeping too, with any degree of regularity, she had stayed very much alive, and she was painfully aware that she would remain so. People didn't die of a broken heart, at least, not these days. If the worst came to the worst, she would be taken into hospital and compulsorily fed, Mrs Heathcliffe had informed her severely, and Helen's bid for immortality had died instead of her mortal self.

Around her, the strangeness of the room provided no comfort. Oh, Heath had transported all her clothes and her personal belongings to his mother's apartment, when Mrs Heathcliffe had agreed, somewhat grudgingly, to accommodate the girl for a few weeks. But she missed the open spaces of Matlock, and the familiarity of the room she had lived in all her conscious life.

Of course, rooms and belongings, even open spaces, were just a symptom of what was really wrong with her, what she really missed. Most of all, she missed Heath, with a desperation that knew no bounds, and every waking moment was a torment, knowing he was never going to take her back.

Sometimes she wondered what she would do, given her time over again. Would she have allowed him to make love to her, knowing what the outcome was going to be? Would she have left him, as he had asked her to do so many times before it became too late?

Mostly, she acknowledged that she wouldn't.

Mostly, she was honest enough with herself to admit that given her time over, she would still have encouraged Heath to make love to her. It was what she had wanted, what she had longed for, since she was old enough to have such feelings. How could she have run away from his lovemaking, when every nerve and sinew in her body had cried out for his fulfilment?

Three weeks ago, when Heath first brought her to stay with his mother, she had prayed every night that she might be carrying Heath's baby. She was convinced that given that ultimatum, he would have been unable to refuse her, and given time, she had convinced herself, he would learn to love her.

But time, and the uninterrupted cycle of her body, quickly destroyed this faint hope, and gradually she came to acknowledge that finding herself pregnant would have solved nothing. She didn't want Heath on those terms. She didn't want him to take her, whether in wedlock or without, just because she was expecting his child, and only the agony of betrayal remained of that fatal night.

A tap at her door heralded Mrs Heathcliffe's entrance, and Heath's mother came into the room, dressed ready for going out.

'I'll be back about six,' she declared, pulling on tan leather driving gloves. 'If you want something to eat, Mrs Henley has left some sandwiches in the kitchen. She'll be back later to prepare dinner, so don't bother to wash your dishes.'

'I don't mind,' Helen said indifferently, but Mrs Heathcliffe was not.

'I know you don't mind,' she declared tartly. 'However, I'd prefer it if you didn't break any more of my bone china. Leave your things for Mrs Henley. She knows how to handle them.'

'Yes, Mrs Heathcliffe.'

Helen slid off the windowseat where she had been

kneeling to face the older woman, and Mrs Heathcliffe's sharp glance flicked appraisingly over her wine-coloured sweater and matching pleated skirt.

'So you'll be all right until I get back,' she demanded, brushing a speck of cotton from the suit covering her ample form. 'Amelia never provides much in the way of refreshment, so when the cards are over, I'll take my leave.'

'Don't hurry on my account,' said Helen stiffly. She was used to Mrs Heathcliffe's regular bridge afternoons, and in all honesty, she welcomed having the apartment to herself.

'Very well.' Heath's mother inclined her head in agreement. 'I'm pleased to see you're learning some manners at last. I can't imagine what they'll make of you at St Helena's. Perhaps it's just as well they're not warned in advance.'

Helen swallowed convulsively. 'Has—has Heath mentioned St Helena's to you recently?' she ventured faintly, realising she had begun to believe she was to remain at the apartment indefinitely.

'Of course.' Mrs Heathcliffe was without compassion. 'Rupert's making arrangements for you to go there at the start of the autumn term in two weeks' time. I forgot—he won't have told you. He only speaks to me when he rings.'

'Two weeks!' Helen said the words disbelievingly, and Mrs Heathcliffe sighed.

'You really must stop behaving as if it was the end of the world, Helen,' she asserted impatiently. 'You've known, ever since Rupert brought you here, that it was only a matter of time before you departed for Switzerland. And not before time, in my opinion. Keeping you at Matlock all these years! I've not known where to show my face.'

Helen bent her head. 'There was nothing wrong with my living at Matlock.'

'When you were a child, perhaps.'

'No.' She looked up. 'When I was an adult. Heath and I—we were happy together.'

'But no longer,' remarked Mrs Heathcliffe acidly. 'For some reason best known to himself, Rupert has at last come to his senses, and I for one am delighted that he's done so before any serious harm was done.'

Helen frowned. 'What do you mean?'

'What do you think I mean, you foolish girl? I may be sixty, but I'm not in my dotage yet. You're—well, you're a reasonably attractive girl, and Rupert was always far too interested in the opposite sex, in my opinion.'

Helen caught her breath. 'Oh, I see. You think— you think perhaps—Heath and I——' Her throat constricted, and she started to laugh, peals of hysterical laughter that rang around the modestly-proportioned bedroom and caused Mrs Heathcliffe to stare at her as if she had gone mad.

'Helen, stop that!' She stepped towards her. 'Stop that at once! I really don't know what's the matter with you, I'm sure I don't. I always said Rupert was a fool for getting himself involved with you. Just because my daughter was reckless enough to marry your father there was no reason for him to take the responsibility for a child that wasn't even his own flesh and blood.'

Helen's laughter died as abruptly as it erupted, and wiping her eyes with her wrists, she turned away. 'Please leave, Mrs Heathcliffe,' she said, wishing desperately that she had a tissue, and Heath's mother uttered a sound of irritation before marching out of the room.

Alone with her thoughts again, Helen left her room to pace restlessly along the corridor to the living room. Mrs Heathcliffe's taste in decoration was not like her

son's. She went in for elaborately-embossed wall
coverings, rooms filled to overflowing with chairs and
tables, and dozens of small ornaments, cluttering up
spaces that would have been better left empty. The
living room was like that: armchairs, sofas, even an
enormous china cabinet to take the overflow from a
collection of occasional tables, all adorned with lacy
cloths to prevent their surfaces from getting scratched.
Mrs Henley, Heath's mother's housekeeper, spent her
days grumbling about the number of articles she had
to move before she could start to dust, and Helen
guessed there were times when she would have liked
to sweep the whole lot on to the heavily patterned
Persian carpet. Helen felt like that now as she curled
up on a striped Regency sofa beside the artificial glow
of the electric fire. She felt sick and miserable and
totally alone. She did not even have the consolation
of a close friend to share her troubles with. Heath
had forbade her to have anything further to do with
either Nigel or Miles, and her girl friends were too
far away to see her now that she was living in
Manchester.

Cupping her chin on one hand, she stared
unseeingly into space. Mrs Heathcliffe's words had
brought the future into perspective, and the prospect
of being sent to school in Switzerland was no longer
just a possibility. Heath was arranging it. She would
probably hear nothing about it until it was time for her
to leave. He would spring it on her, as he had sprung
the news that she was going to stay with his mother
here in Manchester, and Helen's emotions stirred with
belated indignation. She would be eighteen at
Christmas; he had no doubt conveniently forgotten
about that. So far as he was concerned, she was still a
minor, and a liability. What he really wanted was her
off his hands, only he was too polite to say so. What
she should be doing was finding herself a job and

other accommodation, so that when he came along with his plans for her future, she could throw them back in his face.

Pushing herself up from the chair, she made her way back to her own room, rummaging in a drawer for her handbag and pulling out the wallet tucked inside it. When Heath brought her to Manchester, he had given her some money to be going on with. An allowance, he had called it, though Helen had showed little interest in it at the time. Now, however, she withdrew the handful of notes from the leather wallet, counting them swiftly, and with growing jubilation.

There were sixty pounds altogether, in various denominations of notes; sixty pounds, an enormous sum to someone who had never had any real conception of the value of money. Helen was sure that with that amount of money she could easily find herself accommodation until she got a job, and once she was actually earning, she could save up and send it back.

Breathing quickly, she tucked her thumbnail between her teeth, rationalising what she was planning. What she was actually doing was removing herself from Heath's protection, she realised hollowly. If she walked out of this apartment now, she might never see him again, and her legs grew horribly weak at that agonising prospect.

But what were the alternatives? she asked herself fiercely. A school in Switzerland until she was eighteen or even older. And then what? She sighed. She doubted Heath would ever let her return to Matlock. No. Some other arrangement would be made for her, she might even be expected to come back here; and as soon as she showed an interest in some young man, she would be married off as Angela had predicted and consequently out of Heath's hands.

Poor Angela, she reflected ruefully. She hadn't lasted long in her chosen career. Not that she had lost by the deal, Helen amended broodingly. According to Mrs Heathcliffe, her son had given Miss Patterson a very generous bonus, in lieu of the termination of her employment, and Angela would not have to work again for quite a considerable time.

But Angela's good fortune was not hers, and Helen knew that if she was going to do anything with her life it would have to be soon. Two weeks was not long to find a job and somewhere to live, and she intended to do it without any help from anyone.

During the next few days, she spent all her free time combing the employment agencies and visiting various landladies whose advertisements she had read in the local press. Mrs Heathcliffe didn't question her activities. Her own social life was such that Helen's disappearing in the morning, ostensibly to do some shopping, and reappearing again in the afternoon with the same excuse, passed without comment. However, Helen did catch Heath's mother looking at her once or twice with a rather curious expression, and she guessed the older woman was looking forward to her departure.

The job she eventually found was not gained through an agency. It was outlined on a notice stuck in a hairdresser's window, and Helen enquired within as she was requested, and discovered her employer was to be the man who had been so understanding about her own hair.

'I have two salons,' he said, explaining why the notice had been put into this particular window. 'Are you sure you really want this job? I got the impression you were unlikely to be needing the money.'

'You were wrong,' declared Helen, torturing the strap of her handbag. 'It's fifty-six pounds a week, you say? What exactly will I have to do? I've never done anyone's hair before.'

'Oh, my dear, you won't be doing hair!' exclaimed Ricardo impatiently. 'That's why I asked you if you wanted the job. It's really nothing more than charring.'

Helen gave him a rueful smile. 'Honestly, I want it,' she assured him firmly. 'Do you have any idea how difficult it is to get a job, when you've never had any experience at anything?'

'I know,' Ricardo grimaced. 'Okay, young Helen, I'll take you on. Who knows, we may find you have some talent for hairdressing. If you do, I may give you the chance to train.'

'Oh, thank you!' Helen was eternally grateful. 'When do you want me to start?'

'How about tomorrow?' suggested Ricardo drily. 'Come in tomorrow morning, and get the feel of the place. My senior stylist here is Elaine. I'll introduce you now, and you can make your own arrangements.'

'I won't be working with you, then?' Helen asked disappointedly, and Ricardo smiled.

'Not immediately anyway,' he temporised cheerfully. 'But we'll see in the future. I have a girl at my other salon who looks suspiciously as if she's got herself pregnant. If she has and she leaves, I'll see what I can do.'

Helen went back to the apartment that evening feeling amazingly heartened. She had a job, she told herself incredulously, she actually had a job, and all that remained now was for her to find herself a bedsitter, one whose rent would not decimate her fifty-six pounds a week.

She found a place the following afternoon—just a tiny room in a Victorian house not far from the city centre. It was not a particularly salubrious neighbourhood, but at least it was clean and cheap, and Mrs Fairweather, her landlady, seemed sympathetic to her youth.

'You're not from Manchester, are you, lass?' she asked, as they were going downstairs again after seeing the room. 'What's up? You had a barney with your father, have you? I get all kinds of family problems here. But don't you worry, you can tell them I'll see that you get properly fed. Skinny as a lath, you are. Look like you need some good Lancashire hotpot inside you!'

Helen was amazed. Until that moment she had scarcely paid any attention to her appearance, not even noticing that the waistbands of her skirts and pants were looser, or that her face had lost its usual bloom. But walking back to the apartment, she glimpsed her reflection in the plate-glass windows of the department stores, and she realised, with a pang, that she no longer had to worry about counting calories.

'Where have you been?' Mrs Heathcliffe exclaimed, as soon as she let herself into the apartment. 'Rupert's been trying to reach you all afternoon. I told him you'd gone shopping, but he still kept on ringing just the same.'

'Heath?' Helen moistened her dry lips. 'Heath's been ringing me?'

'Haven't I just said so?' Mrs Heathcliffe answered irritably. 'I must have answered that phone half a dozen times. Anyway, he says he's coming to see you tomorrow, so you'd better not be out when he calls.'

Helen put her hand to her throat. 'Tomorrow?' she echoed. 'Did he say why?'

'Something to do with that school in Geneva, I imagine,' declared Mrs Heathcliffe shortly. 'I really didn't ask him. I'm going to be late for my appointment as it is.'

Helen stared at her. 'You're going out?'

'Of course. I told you this morning I was attending a meeting of the bridge club this evening. Surely you haven't forgotten.'

'Oh—no. No.' But in all honesty, she had. In the upheaval of finding herself accommodation, she had completely overlooked Mrs Heathcliffe's arrangements.

'Anyway, Mrs Henley has left you a slice of quiche and some salad in the fridge,' said Heath's mother brusquely. 'As I shall be eating out, I told her not to bother with anything hot. You scarcely eat enough to keep a fly alive as if is. I was sure the quiche would be more than acceptable.'

'Oh, it is. It is,' Helen nodded, her mind racing off at a tangent. If Mrs Heathcliffe was going out this evening, that would mean she would be alone. What a heavensent opportunity to make her escape, particularly with the prospect of Heath's visit looming on the horizon. Of course she would have liked to have seen him—indeed, her heart actually ached at the thought of what she was doing to avoid him. But seeing him again could only cause her more pain, and she had had quite enough of that to be going on with.

Mrs Heathcliffe left just before seven, and Helen cut herself a slice of the quiche to carry into her bedroom and eat while she was packing. She didn't have that much time. She didn't want to be carrying her cases out of the apartment just as Heath's mother returned, and although she was generally quite late home from these occasions, Helen was not about to take any risks.

One case was packed and standing by the front door and the other in the process of being so when the doorbell rang. For a moment, Helen was too shocked to do anything but stand there like a statue, but then, realising it could not be Mrs Heathcliffe home at this time, she hurried to answer it.

Halfway along the hall, another possibility struck her. *Heath*! she thought faintly. It could be Heath on the other side of that door. Oh, God, she prayed fervently, what am I going to do?

She had two options: one, she hid the cases and the evidence of her packing and opened the door; the other, she simply pretended there was no one home. The apartments were not like houses. There was no convenient window to peer through, no betraying light to indicate that someone was in. If she remained perfectly silent, whoever it was might go away, and her heart palpitated wildly as the bell rang again.

What she was not prepared for was what happened next. Instead of her visitor giving up and going away, a key was inserted into the lock, and she watched in horror as the Yale catch turned and the door fell silently inward.

'Helen!'

Heath's harsh use of her name unfroze her locked limbs, and she stepped back uncertainly as he came into the hall. She should have known, she was telling herself fiercely, she should have guessed he might have a key. His mother was not a young woman, and it was reasonable that he should have some means of access in case she fell ill.

'*Helen*!' He saw her as he closed the door, saw her, and the betraying suitcase standing squarely in the hall, and his green eyes grew quite glacial as they comprehended her dilemma.

He looked every bit as forbidding as she had imagined, the black suede pants and matching jacket he was wearing accentuating his grim expression. He looked tired, too, and paler than she remembered, but just as unforgiving as he surveyed her jean-clad form.

'What the hell is going on here?' he demanded, slamming the door and leaning back against it, slipping the key he had used back into his pocket. 'Don't pretend you didn't hear me. It's obvious that you did.'

'I heard you,' she got out faintly, glancing nervously behind her. 'I—I didn't know who could be calling. Your mother's out.'

'I know that.' He straightened away from the door, his eyes appraising her apprehension intently. 'Evidently you knew it, too. Isn't that the meaning of this—little conspiracy?'

'There's no conspiracy.' Helen drew an unsteady breath. 'I—I'm leaving, that's all——'

'The hell you are!'

Brushing past her, Heath strode swiftly along the hall to her room and disappeared inside. She heard the impatient banging of cupboard doors, of her bathroom door being opened and closed, and then he appeared again, more slowly, his dark face worn suddenly, and drawn.

'What have you been doing?' Helen took an involuntary step towards him. 'I haven't stolen anything of your mother's, if that's what you were afraid of. I'm only taking the things that belong to me.'

'I didn't imagine otherwise.' Heath spoke heavily and without heat. 'I just thought—oh, hell, I just thought there must be someone here, someone with you, some person responsible for you packing up and walking out.'

'There is.' Helen held up her head. 'I've got a job—a job in Manchester. It's not much, but I'll have my independence. And I've found somewhere else to live.'

His face grew haggard. 'But why? Why, for God's sake?'

'You know why,' insisted Helen unsteadily. 'I can't go on being dependent on you. And—and I have no intention of going to that school in Switzerland. You can't force me. I'll be eighteen in three months.'

'Oh, for pity's sake!' Heath came back along the hall wearily, stuffing his hands deep into the pockets of his pants. 'You don't have to get a job, if that's all that's troubling you,' he muttered. 'I was coming here this evening to offer you an alternative.'

'You were?' She watched him as he pushed open the door of his mother's overcrowded living room with his foot and walked heavily into the room. 'Well, I don't need your alternatives any longer. I've got an alternative of my own. But I'm glad you've decided that I'm old enough to lead my own life.'

'I didn't say that,' he retorted, as she came to stand in the open doorway. He shook his head, his expression taut. 'On the contrary, I had every intention of keeping you within the sphere of my influence. A friend of my father's, an elderly lady, whose husband died recently, is desperately in need of some young companionship. I was about to suggest that you became her companion. At least, for the winter, until, as you say, you reach your majority.'

'I see.' Helen pressed her palms together. 'Well, that won't be necessary now.'

'What do you intend to do?' Heath spoke roughly, his hands clenching and unclenching inside the taut cloth of his pockets, and she moved her shoulders cautiously.

'I—er—I'm going to work for a hairdresser,' she said, and ignoring his indrawn breath, she went on: 'I've got a room in a house in Prestside.'

'Prestside?' Heath repeated the word savagely, and she nodded.

'I know it's not a particularly nice area, but——'

'Not a particularly nice area!' echoed Heath, with emphasis. 'My God, it's a slum, Helen! No wonder you were planning on running away. You must have known I'd never agree to this.'

'You don't have to agree,' declared Helen doggedly. 'It's my life, not yours.'

'Is that what you believe? Is that what you honestly believe?' he demanded violently. 'For the love of heaven, Helen, I can't let you do this.'

She stared at him steadily. 'You can't stop me,' she averred, even though the knowledge that she was defying him was eating her up. 'You washed your hands of me when you brought me to Manchester. You didn't care about anything but getting me out of your house. You can't expect to go on telling me what to do, when you've made it abundantly clear that you don't really care a damn about me!'

'That is not true.' Heath spoke indistinctly, his voice slurred by some emotion she could not identify. 'It was because I cared about you that I sent you away. Haven't you realised that, you stupid kid!' He turned to rest his arm along the mantel, dislodging a porcelain cupid that smashed heedlessly on to the hearth. 'God, Helen, I don't know how much longer I can keep this up.' He pressed his forehead against his sleeve. 'I need you so badly, I just can't think straight any more.'

She gazed at him disbelievingly. 'I—I don't believe you. This—this is just some—some ruse to get me to do what you want, isn't it?'

'Is it?' He lifted his head and looked at her, and her heart turned over at the naked passion in his eyes. 'Do you want to take a bet on that? I haven't had one decent night's sleep since you left.'

'Oh, Heath!' She was trembling, but still she didn't move and he straightened.

'You're seventeen and I'm thirty-five,' he said huskily. 'For the last three years I've been telling myself that the difference in our ages is too great, that as you grew up and had boy-friends, I'd feel differently. But I didn't.'

Helen shook her head helplessly. 'But why didn't you tell me?'

'Because I intended to fight it,' said Heath harshly. 'Why do you think I've been avoiding you since you came home from school? Why do you think I employed Angela Patterson?'

She gulped. 'I—I thought—because of what other people might say,' she breathed, and he gave her a wry look.

'Since when have I cared what other people said?' he demanded thickly. 'Other people would have had me put you in a children's home. Other people considered our relationship almost indecent.' He bent his head. 'I was determined that it wouldn't be so.'

'Oh, Heath!' Helen spread her hands. 'But you sent me away.'

'After seducing you, yes,' he agreed flatly. 'I didn't admire myself for that. You were right—just then, I did want you out of the house. Loving you was an addiction I had no intention of satisfying.'

'But—but why?'

'For God's sake, Helen, I thought I was doing the right thing. I knew I couldn't keep you with me, and marrying you seemed out of the question. I thought— oh, I don't know what I thought. I guess it did cross my mind that if I could send you away for a while we might both come to our senses, but God help me, it didn't work. These past weeks have been hell on earth, and I came here this evening with the intention, as I said, of fixing you up as Mrs Golightly's companion.'

'Mrs Golightly?' Helen blinked. 'But—she just lives across the river——'

'—about three miles from Matlock. That's right,' agreed Heath heavily. 'Far enough to be out of temptation, but near enough for me to keep an eye on you, and on the people you associate with.'

She caught her lower lip between her teeth. 'It's been hell for me, too.' She paused. 'I've lost weight. Haven't you noticed?'

'I noticed,' he said huskily. 'I noticed everything about you in those minutes when I thought you must have got involved with some other man.'

'Were you jealous?'

She couldn't resist the question, and his lips twisted. 'What do you think?' he demanded. 'If I could be jealous of Fox and young Ormerod, then yes, I think you could say I'd be jealous of any competition.'

She made a little sound of exhilaration. 'You were jealous of Miles?' She shook her head. 'He said you were, but I didn't believe him.'

'I guess he's more perceptive than I thought,' said Heath quietly. 'So—what are you going to do now? Do you still want to go ahead and take this job.'

Helen half turned to rest her spine against the frame of the door, her limbs shaking so much, she could hardly support herself. 'What—what is the alternative?' she whispered, looking at him out of the corners of her eyes, and with a muffled oath, Heath crossed the space between them.

He halted right beside her, so close that the arm she had raised to rest against the opposite framework of the door was brushing his chest. Then, with evident restraint, he lifted her hand from its position and raised it to his lips, taking each of her fingers into his mouth in turn, depositing a kiss on each.

'The alternative,' he said, somewhat constrictedly, 'is that you could marry me at Christmas.'

'At Christmas?' Helen's cry was a protest.

'Yes, at Christmas,' he affirmed huskily, his mouth against her palm. 'Then no one can say you were not old enough to make your own decision. Always assuming you accept my proposal, of course.'

She expelled her breath unsteadily. 'Of course I accept your proposal,' she exclaimed, looping her other arm round his neck. 'Oh, Heath!' this as he gathered her close against him. 'Oh, Heath, why must we wait so long?'

'We—oh, God!—we don't have to wait to be together,' he muttered unevenly, his mouth finding the parting of hers. 'I—I may be diligent in some ways, but that is not one of them. Indeed,' his fingers slid beneath her hair to cradle the vulnerable curve of her nape, 'the way I feel right now, I don't think I can wait until I get you back to Matlock.'

'You're taking me back to Matlock?' she breathed eagerly. 'When? *When*?'

'Tonight?' he suggested unsteadily. 'Or am I asking too much?'

'Too much?' Helen shook her head, burrowing against him urgently, sliding her arms about his waist inside his jacket with compulsive abandon. 'But I shall have to explain the situation to Ricardo.'

'Ricardo?'

Heath drew back to look at her, and she gave a helpless little grimace. 'The hairdresser who has employed me. The one Angela wanted to cut my hair, as it happens.'

'Angela wanted you to get your hair cut?' Heath interceded harshly, and she nodded.

'Ricardo said it would be a shame——'

'Damn right!' His hand slid possessively into the silken mass of curls. 'If I'd known——'

'You'd probably have agreed with her,' said Helen ruefully, and he expelled his breath heavily.

'I've been a brute, haven't I?'

'Some,' she admitted unsteadily, and he covered her mouth with his with increasing hunger.

'Leave—Ricardo to me,' he told her thickly. 'Right now, I'm not thinking very coherently. What time did you say my mother was due back?'

Some time later, Helen opened her eyes to find Heath propped on his elbow beside her in her bed, regarding her with unconcealed possession. 'You know, you're the only female I know who looks good without any make-up,' he remarked, touching his tongue to the corner of her mouth.

'And you've known quite a few,' murmured Helen sleepily, reaching up to link her arms about his neck.

'Some,' he agreed honestly, submitting to her demands. 'And don't do that, my darling, or my dear mama may come back and find us *in flagrante delicto*.'

'Do you mind?' Helen was still bemused from his lovemaking, and he drew back to give her a wry smile.

'No,' he conceded, 'I don't mind. But I think discovering we are planning to get married is enough of a shock for one night, don't you? And in any case, you've got to finish your packing. We're leaving as soon as I've explained.'

'She's going to be surprised,' murmured Helen as he released her. Then, sliding reluctantly out of bed, she paced over to the mirror. 'Hmm, you know I used to wish you'd made me pregnant, so you'd have to marry me,' she admitted provocatively. 'Now I'm glad you didn't. You might not love me if I was fat.'

'I'd love you whatever you looked like,' retorted Heath, getting out of bed to come and join her, drawing her back against his muscled body so that their reflections mingled. 'Remember, I've known you in pigtails and braces, as well as you are now.' He brushed her hair with his lips and then pushed her away from him. 'So—put some clothes on, will you? Go on, do it. Or I won't be held responsible for my actions!'

She and Heath were married on the twenty-third of December, and spent Christmas in London with Marion and Greg Marsden and their family before flying to Nice, and Heath's villa on the shores of the Mediterrranean. It was a rather grey Mediterranean at this time of the year, but they were not particularly interested in their surroundings. The privacy of the villa was all they required, and only occasionally did they venture out to walk along the sands at low tide.

Heath's mother had attended the wedding, somewhat reluctantly, before joining a conducted tour of Egypt, which she and some of her cronies had arranged. She had taken no part in the organising of the wedding, she had left all that to Heath, but she was quite prepared to stand beside them at the reception, and receive everyone's congratulations for Heath's having found himself such a beautiful bride.

'I really believe she's quite relieved to see me married at last,' Heath remarked one morning, as they lingered over the leisurely breakfast which Clothilde, the elderly maid, had prepared for them. 'I think she'd suspected for some time exactly what was stopping me.'

'Me,' murmured Helen mischievously, cupping her chin on her hand and surveying him with unconcealed satisfaction. 'Perhaps she was afraid I might seduce you.'

He regarded her tolerantly. 'With good reason, as it happens,' he remarked drily. 'I didn't stand a chance.'

'Are you sorry?' She arched her dark brows.

'Are you?'

'Oh, yes——' and at his look of disconcertment, she gave a soft laugh. 'I'm sorry we didn't do this a year ago,' she finished huskily. 'But you didn't answer my question.'

'What do you think?'

'You tell me.'

'What?' The green eyes, which had once been so unpredictable, narrowed caressingly. 'That I love you more than I thought it was possible to love another human being? That I was crazy for ever thinking I could live without you?'

'That will do to be going on with,' she said breathily. 'Let's go back to bed, hmm? I don't feel like getting dressed just now, do you?'

Heath's smile was sardonic. 'You can't still be tired,' he remarked provokingly. 'These last few days——'

'Stop teasing!' Helen reached out and captured his hand, carrying it to her lips deliberately, keeping her eyes on his as she did so. 'Don't you feel the tiniest bit lazy?'

'With you around?' He grimaced, but his eyes darkened as emotion stirred in spite of himself. 'All right,' he said unevenly, 'let's go back to bed. We can talk later.'

'All the days of our lives,' agreed Helen, as he swung her up into his arms, and Heath did not disagree with her.

Unwrap romance this Christmas

A Love Affair
LINDSAY ARMSTRONG

Valentine's Night
PENNY JORDAN

Man on the Make
ROBERTA LEIGH

Rendezvous in Rio
ELIZABETH OLDFIELD

Put some more romance into your Christmas, with four brand new titles from Mills & Boon in this stylish gift pack.

They make great holiday reading, and for only £5.40, it makes an ideal gift.

The special gift pack is available from 6th October. Look out for it at Boots, Martins, John Menzies, W.H. Smith, Woolworths and other paperback stockists.

Mills & Boon

ROMANCING
THE PHONE

Win the romantic holiday of a lifetime for two at the exclusive Couples Hotel in Ocho Rios on Jamaica's north coast with the Mills & Boon and British Telecom's novel competition, 'Romancing the Phone'.

This exciting competition looks at the importance the telephone call plays in romance. All you have to do is write a story or extract about a romance involving the phone which lasts approximately two minutes when read aloud.

The winner will not only receive the holiday in Jamaica, but the entry will also be heard by millions of people when it is included in a selection of extracts from a short list of entries on British Telecom's 'Romance Line'. Regional winners and runners up will receive British Telecom telephones, answer machines and Mills & Boon books.

For an entry leaflet and further details all you have to do is call 01 400 5359, or write to 'Romancing the Phone', 22 Endell Street, London WC2H 9AD.
You may be mailed with other offers as a result of this application.

British
TELECOM

A SPARKLING COLLECTION
FOR CHRISTMAS FROM

TEMPTATION

This special Temptation Christmas pack has 4 novels all based on a single theme – the Montclair Emeralds. Enjoy and discover the exciting mystique and the secrets of these magnificent gems.

The pack features four of our most popular authors.

Fulfilment	–	Barbara Delinsky
Trust	–	Rita Clay Estrada
Joy	–	Jayne Ann Krentz
Impulse	–	Vicki.Lewis Thompson

PLUS, with each pack you have a chance to enter the fabulous Temptation Emeralds competition.

Available from Boots, Martins, John Menzies, WH Smith, Woolworths and other paperback stockists.

Pub. Date
3rd November 1989

 Mills & Boon

Price £5.40